Contents

Houghton Mifflin Mathematics

Practice Activities

Authors

Lelon R. Capps
University of Kansas
Lawrence, Kansas

W. G. Quast
Slippery Rock University
Slippery Rock, Pennsylvania

Mary Ann Haubner
Mount Saint Joseph College
Cincinnati, Ohio

William L. Cole
Michigan State University
East Lansing, Michigan

Leland Webb
California State College
Bakersfield, California

Charles E. Allen
Los Angeles Unified
  School District
Los Angeles, California

Coordinating Author

Ernest R. Duncan
Professor Emeritus
Rutgers University
New Brunswick, New Jersey

Houghton Mifflin Company   BOSTON

Atlanta   Dallas   Geneva, Ill.   Palo Alto   Princeton   Toronto

Credits

Cover photography by Lehman Millet Incorporated
Text design by Ligature, Inc.
Art and Production by Ligature, Inc.

Illustration

Ruth Roman Brunke   6, 22, 25, 76, 80, 103, 108, 120, 130, 133, 134, 135
Rondi Collette   115 (top), 117
Shelley Dieterichs   89, 102,
Creston Ely   87, 91
Judy Friedman   90
Walter Gaffney-Kessel   15, 27, 29, 41, 43, 45, 49
Rich Lo   2, 5, 13, 17, 18, 19, 50, 52, 56 (bottom), 58, 62, 69, 83, 92, 96, 104, 106, 107, 109, 111, 112, 115 (middle), 116, 118, 126, 127, 136
Garry Matusek   16, 21, 23, 32, 33, 36, 39, 44, 46, 113, 114, 121, 122, 129, 132
Jeff O'Connor   14, 28, 30, 31, 34, 37, 38, 51, 54, 55, 56 (top), 57, 60, 63, 65, 67, 68, 71

1989 Impression

Printed in U.S.A.

ISBN: 0–395–38644–6

IJ-WC-954321

Name _____

Student Book pp. 2–3

1-1

Add.

1. $6 + 5 =$ _____   2. $1 + 9 =$ _____   3. $2 + 7 =$ _____   4. $8 + 1 =$ _____

5. $2 + 5 =$ _____   6. $4 + 3 =$ _____   7. $5 + 5 =$ _____   8. $5 + 6 =$ _____

9. $5 + 8 =$ _____   10. $9 + 7 =$ _____   11. $8 + 8 =$ _____   12. $6 + 3 =$ _____

13. $6 + 0 =$ _____   14. $1 + 1 =$ _____   15. $7 + 1 =$ _____   16. $2 + 6 =$ _____

17. $9 \atop +8$	18. $4 \atop +0$	19. $8 \atop +4$	20. $3 \atop +7$	21. $7 \atop +4$	22. $0 \atop +1$
23. $6 \atop +7$	24. $9 \atop +5$	25. $7 \atop +9$	26. $0 \atop +0$	27. $1 \atop +3$	28. $5 \atop +0$
29. $4 \atop +4$	30. $3 \atop +9$	31. $8 \atop +2$	32. $3 \atop +0$	33. $9 \atop +2$	34. $6 \atop +6$
35. $6 \atop +1$	36. $7 \atop +3$	37. $8 \atop +7$	38. $9 \atop +6$	39. $4 \atop +8$	40. $7 \atop +6$
41. $9 \atop +9$	42. $0 \atop +7$	43. $0 \atop +9$	44. $4 \atop +6$	45. $5 \atop +4$	46. $2 \atop +2$
47. $4 \atop +2$	48. $5 \atop +9$	49. $6 \atop +2$	50. $7 \atop +7$	51. $2 \atop +9$	52. $5 \atop +3$
53. $5 \atop +1$	54. $4 \atop +7$	55. $2 \atop +3$	56. $7 \atop +2$	57. $3 \atop +8$	58. $9 \atop +4$

Copyright © Houghton Mifflin Company
All rights reserved. Printed in U.S.A./4

1 PA

Practice

Student Book pp. 4–5

Changing the order of the addends does not change the sum.
This is called the Order Property of Addition.

$7 + 3 = 10$

$3 + 7 = 10$

Changing the grouping of the addends does not change
the sum.
This is called the Grouping Property of Addition.

$$\begin{array}{c} \boxed{\begin{array}{c} 3 \\ 4 \end{array}} \rightarrow \begin{array}{c} 7 \\ +6 \\ \hline 13 \end{array} \end{array} \qquad \begin{array}{c} 3 \\ \boxed{\begin{array}{c} 4 \\ 6 \end{array}} \rightarrow \begin{array}{c} 3 \\ +10 \\ \hline 13 \end{array} \end{array}$$

Add.

1. $\begin{array}{r} 4 \\ +3 \\ \hline \end{array}$
2. $\begin{array}{r} 6 \\ +2 \\ \hline \end{array}$
3. $\begin{array}{r} 8 \\ +1 \\ \hline \end{array}$
4. $\begin{array}{r} 7 \\ +3 \\ \hline \end{array}$
5. $\begin{array}{r} 5 \\ +6 \\ \hline \end{array}$
6. $\begin{array}{r} 9 \\ +2 \\ \hline \end{array}$

7. $\begin{array}{r} 4 \\ +8 \\ \hline \end{array}$
8. $\begin{array}{r} 6 \\ +9 \\ \hline \end{array}$
9. $\begin{array}{r} 3 \\ +1 \\ \hline \end{array}$
10. $\begin{array}{r} 8 \\ +6 \\ \hline \end{array}$
11. $\begin{array}{r} 9 \\ +9 \\ \hline \end{array}$
12. $\begin{array}{r} 4 \\ +9 \\ \hline \end{array}$

13. $\begin{array}{r} 6 \\ +7 \\ \hline \end{array}$
14. $\begin{array}{r} 2 \\ +0 \\ \hline \end{array}$
15. $\begin{array}{r} 9 \\ +8 \\ \hline \end{array}$
16. $\begin{array}{r} 3 \\ +7 \\ \hline \end{array}$
17. $\begin{array}{r} 4 \\ +5 \\ \hline \end{array}$
18. $\begin{array}{r} 3 \\ +6 \\ \hline \end{array}$

19. $\begin{array}{r} 5 \\ 1 \\ +6 \\ \hline \end{array}$
20. $\begin{array}{r} 9 \\ 3 \\ +2 \\ \hline \end{array}$
21. $\begin{array}{r} 8 \\ 7 \\ +4 \\ \hline \end{array}$
22. $\begin{array}{r} 3 \\ 0 \\ +5 \\ \hline \end{array}$
23. $\begin{array}{r} 1 \\ 9 \\ +5 \\ \hline \end{array}$
24. $\begin{array}{r} 6 \\ 4 \\ +4 \\ \hline \end{array}$

Solve.

25. Charles bought 6 books. Rachel
bought 4 books. Who bought more
books, Charles or Rachel?

_____

26. Lori has 3 goldfish, Carla has 4
goldfish, and Ron has 7 goldfish.
How many goldfish are there in
all? _____

Practice

1-3

Try to add numbers in your head. When you add greater numbers, look for patterns to make mental math easier. Here's how to add ____ 27 in your head.

$$+\ 4$$

Think

$$
\begin{array}{ccccccc}
7 & \text{ten more} \longrightarrow & 17 & \text{ten more} \longrightarrow & 27 \\
+\ 4 & & +\ 4 & & +\ 4 \\
\hline
11 & \text{ten more} \longrightarrow & 21 & \text{ten more} \longrightarrow & 31
\end{array}
$$

Use mental math to add.

1. a. $\begin{array}{r} 3 \\ +5 \\ \hline \end{array}$ **b.** $\begin{array}{r} 13 \\ +\ 5 \\ \hline \end{array}$ **c.** $\begin{array}{r} 23 \\ +\ 5 \\ \hline \end{array}$ **2. a.** $\begin{array}{r} 6 \\ +3 \\ \hline \end{array}$ **b.** $\begin{array}{r} 16 \\ +\ 3 \\ \hline \end{array}$ **c.** $\begin{array}{r} 26 \\ +\ 3 \\ \hline \end{array}$

3. a. $\begin{array}{r} 5 \\ +7 \\ \hline \end{array}$ **b.** $\begin{array}{r} 25 \\ +\ 7 \\ \hline \end{array}$ **c.** $\begin{array}{r} 45 \\ +\ 7 \\ \hline \end{array}$ **4. a.** $\begin{array}{r} 8 \\ +9 \\ \hline \end{array}$ **b.** $\begin{array}{r} 18 \\ +\ 9 \\ \hline \end{array}$ **c.** $\begin{array}{r} 48 \\ +\ 9 \\ \hline \end{array}$

5. $\begin{array}{r} 11 \\ +\ 9 \\ \hline \end{array}$ **6.** $\begin{array}{r} 14 \\ +\ 8 \\ \hline \end{array}$ **7.** $\begin{array}{r} 16 \\ +\ 7 \\ \hline \end{array}$ **8.** $\begin{array}{r} 22 \\ +\ 6 \\ \hline \end{array}$ **9.** $\begin{array}{r} 32 \\ +\ 8 \\ \hline \end{array}$ **10.** $\begin{array}{r} 31 \\ +\ 4 \\ \hline \end{array}$

11. $\begin{array}{r} 3 \\ 7 \\ +2 \\ \hline \end{array}$ **12.** $\begin{array}{r} 6 \\ 2 \\ +3 \\ \hline \end{array}$ **13.** $\begin{array}{r} 1 \\ 7 \\ +8 \\ \hline \end{array}$ **14.** $\begin{array}{r} 1 \\ 5 \\ 4 \\ +7 \\ \hline \end{array}$ **15.** $\begin{array}{r} 2 \\ 8 \\ 4 \\ +3 \\ \hline \end{array}$ **16.** $\begin{array}{r} 6 \\ 3 \\ 5 \\ +9 \\ \hline \end{array}$

17. $5 + 2 + 3 =$ ____   **18.** $9 + 6 + 5 =$ ____   **19.** $8 + 3 + 5 =$ ____

20. $6 + 7 + 1 =$ ____   **21.** $9 + 1 + 2 + 3 =$ ____   **22.** $7 + 2 + 3 + 5 =$ ____

Write a number sentence for each problem. Then solve.

23. Mrs. Jones planted 3 apple trees, 4 peach trees and 2 cherry trees. How many fruit trees did she plant in all?

_____

_____

24. Mark worked 3 hours on Monday. He worked 4 hours on Tuesday, 6 hours on Wednesday, and 4 hours on Thursday. How many hours did he work in four days?

_____

_____

Practice

Student Book pp. 8–9

Subtract.

1. $15 - 7 =$ ___
2. $7 - 4 =$ ___
3. $9 - 2 =$ ___
4. $8 - 5 =$ ___

5. $5 - 0 =$ ___
6. $6 - 1 =$ ___
7. $16 - 9 =$ ___
8. $15 - 8 =$ ___

9. $14 - 5 =$ ___
10. $7 - 6 =$ ___
11. $4 - 4 =$ ___
12. $6 - 2 =$ ___

13. $8 - 0 =$ ___
14. $9 - 1 =$ ___
15. $8 - 4 =$ ___
16. $7 - 2 =$ ___

17. $\begin{array}{r}11\\-6\\\hline\end{array}$	18. $\begin{array}{r}13\\-9\\\hline\end{array}$	19. $\begin{array}{r}14\\-7\\\hline\end{array}$	20. $\begin{array}{r}17\\-9\\\hline\end{array}$	21. $\begin{array}{r}12\\-3\\\hline\end{array}$	22. $\begin{array}{r}7\\-7\\\hline\end{array}$
23. $\begin{array}{r}11\\-8\\\hline\end{array}$	24. $\begin{array}{r}6\\-0\\\hline\end{array}$	25. $\begin{array}{r}10\\-7\\\hline\end{array}$	26. $\begin{array}{r}11\\-2\\\hline\end{array}$	27. $\begin{array}{r}15\\-6\\\hline\end{array}$	28. $\begin{array}{r}18\\-9\\\hline\end{array}$
29. $\begin{array}{r}8\\-6\\\hline\end{array}$	30. $\begin{array}{r}12\\-8\\\hline\end{array}$	31. $\begin{array}{r}9\\-4\\\hline\end{array}$	32. $\begin{array}{r}1\\-1\\\hline\end{array}$	33. $\begin{array}{r}4\\-3\\\hline\end{array}$	34. $\begin{array}{r}5\\-2\\\hline\end{array}$
35. $\begin{array}{r}6\\-3\\\hline\end{array}$	36. $\begin{array}{r}13\\-4\\\hline\end{array}$	37. $\begin{array}{r}9\\-6\\\hline\end{array}$	38. $\begin{array}{r}10\\-1\\\hline\end{array}$	39. $\begin{array}{r}12\\-4\\\hline\end{array}$	40. $\begin{array}{r}11\\-7\\\hline\end{array}$
41. $\begin{array}{r}10\\-8\\\hline\end{array}$	42. $\begin{array}{r}12\\-8\\\hline\end{array}$	43. $\begin{array}{r}5\\-4\\\hline\end{array}$	44. $\begin{array}{r}12\\-7\\\hline\end{array}$	45. $\begin{array}{r}13\\-5\\\hline\end{array}$	46. $\begin{array}{r}6\\-2\\\hline\end{array}$
47. $\begin{array}{r}14\\-8\\\hline\end{array}$	48. $\begin{array}{r}13\\-7\\\hline\end{array}$	49. $\begin{array}{r}16\\-8\\\hline\end{array}$	50. $\begin{array}{r}12\\-6\\\hline\end{array}$	51. $\begin{array}{r}14\\-9\\\hline\end{array}$	52. $\begin{array}{r}10\\-4\\\hline\end{array}$
53. $\begin{array}{r}15\\-9\\\hline\end{array}$	54. $\begin{array}{r}9\\-0\\\hline\end{array}$	55. $\begin{array}{r}7\\-4\\\hline\end{array}$	56. $\begin{array}{r}13\\-8\\\hline\end{array}$	57. $\begin{array}{r}9\\-5\\\hline\end{array}$	58. $\begin{array}{r}10\\-3\\\hline\end{array}$

Use addition facts to help you subtract. Learn to build a fact family.

$7 + 4 = 11$

$4 + 7 = 11$

$11 - 4 = 7$

$11 - 7 = 4$

Add or subtract.

1. a. $6 + 9 =$ _____

   b. $15 - 9 =$ _____

   c. $9 + 6 =$ _____

   d. $15 - 6 =$ _____

2. a. $5 + 3 =$ _____

   b. $8 - 3 =$ _____

   c. $3 + 5 =$ _____

   d. $8 - 5 =$ _____

3. a. $0 + 4 =$ _____

   b. $4 - 4 =$ _____

   c. $4 + 0 =$ _____

   d. $4 - 0 =$ _____

4. $\begin{array}{r} 7 \\ + 5 \\ \hline \end{array}$
  5. $\begin{array}{r} 8 \\ + 9 \\ \hline \end{array}$
  6. $\begin{array}{r} 4 \\ + 5 \\ \hline \end{array}$
  7. $\begin{array}{r} 10 \\ - 4 \\ \hline \end{array}$
  8. $\begin{array}{r} 16 \\ - 8 \\ \hline \end{array}$
  9. $\begin{array}{r} 7 \\ + 7 \\ \hline \end{array}$

10. $\begin{array}{r} 8 \\ + 5 \\ \hline \end{array}$
  11. $\begin{array}{r} 13 \\ - 7 \\ \hline \end{array}$
  12. $\begin{array}{r} 14 \\ - 8 \\ \hline \end{array}$
  13. $\begin{array}{r} 5 \\ + 5 \\ \hline \end{array}$
  14. $\begin{array}{r} 12 \\ - 8 \\ \hline \end{array}$
  15. $\begin{array}{r} 3 \\ + 6 \\ \hline \end{array}$

Complete the number sentence to solve the problem. Then write the other facts in the fact family.

16. Inez has drawn 9 posters. Martina has drawn 4 more posters than Inez. How many posters has Martina drawn?

_____ + _____ = _____

_____

_____

_____

17. Michael has 14 spelling words to memorize. He can spell 8 of the words. How many does he have left to memorize?

_____ − _____ = _____

_____

_____

_____

Practice

Student Book pp. 12–13

The performing seal can do 5 tricks. The dancing bear can do 9 tricks. How many more tricks can the bear do? The four steps below can help you solve the problem.

1 Understand the problem.	What do you know? What do you want to know?	Bear—9 tricks Seal—5 tricks How many more tricks?
2 Make a plan.	What do you do to solve the problem?	To find how many more, you subtract 5 from 9.
3 Use the plan to do the work.	Show your work.	9 −5 —— 4
4 Answer and check for sense.	Check to be sure your answer makes sense.	4 tricks 4 + 5 = 9 ✔

Write *add* or *subtract* for your plan. Then solve.

1. The Great Manzini pulls 8 rabbits out of his hat. He then pulls 4 doves out of his coat. How many animals does he have in all? _____

2. He pulls 6 canaries out of his sleeve. He makes 2 disappear. How many canaries are left? _____

3. A juggler keeps 3 balls and 2 clubs in the air. How many things does she juggle at once? _____

4. The lion tamer has 7 tigers. While 2 do tricks the others rest. How many tigers are resting? _____

5. There are 13 acrobats and 7 tumblers in the circus. How many more acrobats than tumblers are there? _____

6. There are 11 trained monkeys. Only 5 ride bicycles. How many do not ride bicycles? _____

Practice

Student Book pp. 14–15

1-7

The ten digits are 0, 1, 2, 3, 4, 5, 6, 7, 8, 9.
We use them to write any number.

hundreds	tens	ones
2	4	7

The **standard form** is 247.
We read 247 as two hundred forty-seven.
The **expanded form** is 200 + 40 + 7.

The digit 2 is in the hundreds' place. Its value is 200.
The digit 4 is in the tens' place. Its value is 40.
The digit 7 is in the ones' place. Its value is 7.

Write the standard form.

1. 6 ones _____

2. 5 tens 4 ones _____

3. 5 hundreds 7 tens 8 ones _____

4. 6 hundreds 1 ten _____

5. 8 hundreds 3 ones _____

6. 7 hundreds 6 tens 5 ones _____

7. 4 hundreds _____

8. 1 hundred 2 ones _____

9. 2 hundreds 1 ten 3 ones _____

10. 9 hundreds 3 tens 3 ones _____

11. five hundred twenty-seven _____

12. six hundred thirty-two _____

13. nine hundred one _____

14. five hundred twenty _____

15. four hundred ninety-six _____

16. eight hundred thirteen _____

Write the expanded form.

17. 659

18. 430

19. 774

_____   _____   _____

Unscramble the numbers. Write the standard form.

20. 2 tens
8 hundreds
5 ones

21. 2 ones
8 tens
5 hundreds

22. 2 hundreds
8 ones
5 tens

_____   _____   _____

Practice

1-8

Look at this number.

thousands	hundreds	tens	ones
1	3	0	4

The digit 1 is in the thousands' place. Its value is 1000.
The standard form is 1304.
We read 1304 as one thousand three hundred four.
We write 1304 in expanded form as 1000 + 300 + 4.

Write the value of the underlined digit.

1. 5321 _____   **2.** 5862 _____   **3.** 8106 _____   **4.** 1234 _____

5. 9471 _____   **6.** 6357 _____   **7.** 2140 _____   **8.** 5918 _____

Write the standard form.

9. 6 thousands
4 hundreds
3 tens
1 one

_____

10. 4 thousands
2 hundreds
9 tens
6 ones

_____

11. 9 thousands
6 hundreds
1 ten
2 ones

_____

12. 2 thousands
3 hundreds
6 tens
7 ones

_____

13. six thousand nine _____

14. 7 thousand 2 tens 4 ones _____

Write the number in expanded form.

15. 4361

16. 8088

_____

_____

Draw a line to the answer that makes sense.

17. A bear can live to be ☐ years old.   2

18. Some birds migrate ☐ miles.   20

19. An elementary school has ☐ students.   200

20. A dog stands ☐ feet high.   2000

Name _____

Look at these numbers.

A. | 5 | 4 | 3 | 2 | 8 | 6 |

B. | 2 | 1 | 6 | 3 | 3 | 2 | 0 | 0 | 0 |

A. We read 543,286 as five hundred forty-three thousand, two hundred eighty-six.
The value of the digit 3 is 3000.
The value of the digit 4 is 40,000.
The value of the digit 5 is 500,000.

B. We read 216,332,000 as two hundred sixteen million, three hundred thirty-two thousand.
The value of the digit 6 is 6,000,000 (6 million).
The value of the digit 1 is 10,000,000 (10 million).
The value of the digit 2 is 200,000,000 (200 million).

Write the value of the underlined digit.

1. 534,208 _____

2. 603,246 _____

3. 867,372,413 _____

4. 483,296 _____

5. 846,432 _____

6. 874,578,132 _____

Write the standard form.

7. 36 thousand _____

8. 86 thousand, 326 _____

9. 720 thousand _____

10. 270 thousand, 637 _____

11. 132 million _____

12. 398 million, 799 _____

13. 413 million, 342 thousand, 482   _____

14. seventy-four thousand, three hundred forty-one   _____

15. four hundred twenty-five million, one hundred five thousand   _____

16. one hundred ninety thousand, six hundred two   _____

17. two hundred million, four hundred thousand   _____

Choose the number that is different. Write a, b, or c. Name the places of the digits that are different.

18. a. 846,251   **b.** 846,251   **c.** 864,251

_____

19. a. 389,742   **b.** 839,742   **c.** 839,742

_____

Name _____

Compare 6283 and 6259.
First compare the thousands.
Next compare the hundreds.
Then compare the tens.

thousands	hundreds	tens	ones
6	2	8	3
6	2	5	9

↑ same   ↑ same   ↑ The tens are different.

8 tens are greater than 5 tens.

8 tens > 5 tens

so, 6283 > 6259

Compare 4321 and 987.
First compare the thousands.

thousands	hundreds	tens	ones
4	3	2	1
	9	8	7

↑

The thousands are different.

4 thousands are greater than 0 thousands

4 thousands > 0 thousands

so, 4321 > 987

Compare the numbers. Write <, >, or =.

1. 9 ___ 6
2. 67 ___ 79
3. 408 ___ 480
4. 492 ___ 274

5. 350 ___ 305
6. 821 ___ 812
7. 515 ___ 515
8. 317 ___ 713

9. 908 ___ 809
10. 711 ___ 721
11. 612 ___ 617
12. 504 ___ 419

13. 5315 ___ 6315
14. 7104 ___ 7124
15. 706 ___ 617
16. 3410 ___ 3410

17. 46,834 ___ 83,642
18. 543,782 ___ 543,287

Write the numbers in order from greatest to least.

19. 436   842   673
20. 37,846   36,820   38,102

_____   _____

Use all the digits to write the least and the greatest numbers.

	digits	least number	greatest number
21.	1,3,7		
22.	9,1,4,7		

Name _____

Write the results when the Rounding Machine follows these directions.

Round the two-digit numbers to the nearest ten.
Round the three-digit numbers to the nearest hundred.
Round the four-digit numbers to the nearest thousand.

Two-digit numbers		Three-digit numbers		Four-digit numbers	
1.	13	8.	154	15.	1681
2.	36	9.	264	16.	2052
3.	68	10.	338	17.	6079
4.	85	11.	405	18.	5455
5.	47	12.	665	19.	4891
6.	71	13.	270	20.	3572
7.	92	14.	918	21.	7806

The Nearest Ten	The Nearest Hundred	The Nearest Thousand
1. _____	8. _____	15. _____
2. _____	9. _____	16. _____
3. _____	10. _____	17. _____
4. _____	11. _____	18. _____
5. _____	12. _____	19. _____
6. _____	13. _____	20. _____
7. _____	14. _____	21. _____

Rounding Machine

Name _____

To round a number to a certain place, look at the digit to the right of that place.

Round 486 to the nearest ten. 4<u>8</u>6	The digit to the right of the tens is 6.	Is this digit 5 or more? Yes	Round 486 up to 490.
Round 2739 to the nearest hundred. 2<u>7</u>39	The digit to the right of the hundreds is 3.	Is this digit 5 or more? No	Round 2739 down to 2700.
Round 51,924 to the nearest thousand. 5<u>1</u>,924	The digit to the right of the thousands is 9.	Is this digit 5 or more? Yes	Round 51,924 up to 52,000.
Round 6489 to the greatest place value. <u>6</u>489	The digit to the right of the greatest place value is 4.	Is the digit 5 or more? No	Round 6489 down to 6000.

Round to the nearest ten.

1. 358 _____   2. 451 _____   3. 692 _____   4. 247 _____   5. 183 _____

6. 764 _____   7. 229 _____   8. 565 _____   9. 322 _____   10. 641 _____

Round to the nearest hundred.

11. 2936 _____   12. 5721 _____   13. 4690 _____   14. 6311 _____   15. 3542 _____

16. 1768 _____   17. 8330 _____   18. 7263 _____   19. 9115 _____   20. 5289 _____

Round to the nearest thousand.

21. 35,846 _____   22. 18,274 _____   23. 59,703 _____   24. 43,520 _____

25. 89,500 _____   26. 27,249 _____   27. 12,876 _____   28. 74,850 _____

Round to the greatest place value.

29. 73 _____   30. 28 _____   31. 236 _____   32. 576 _____

33. 48,934 _____   34. 68,432 _____   35. 876 _____   36. 6219 _____

Name

Allison asked each of her fourth-grade classmates to name a favorite pet. She made a bar graph to show the results. The graph shows that 9 students would like to own a dog.

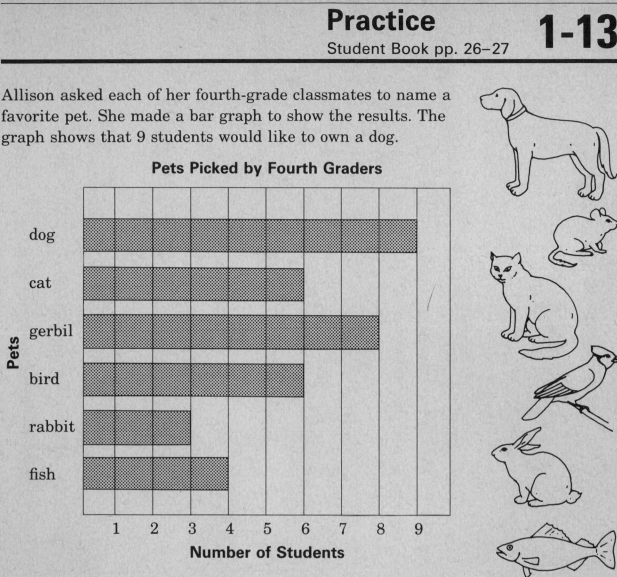

Pets Picked by Fourth Graders

Use the graph to answer the questions.

1. What is the title of the bar graph? _____

2. What do the numbers on the bottom of the graph mean? _____

3. What does each bar on the graph stand for? _____

4. How many students would like to own a fish? _____

5. Which pet would 3 students like to own? _____

6. Which two pets would each like to be owned by 6 students? _____

7. Which pet would the least number of students like to own? _____

8. Which pet would the greatest number of students like to own? _____

9. How many more students chose a gerbil than a cat? _____

10. How many students are in Allison's class? _____

Practice

Student Book pp. 36–37

Add 15 and 36.

Add the ones.
Rename 11 ones as 1 ten 1 one.

$$\begin{array}{r} 1 \\ 15 \\ +36 \\ \hline 1 \end{array}$$

Add the tens.

$$\begin{array}{r} 1 \\ 15 \\ +36 \\ \hline 51 \end{array}$$

Add.

1. $\begin{array}{r} 14 \\ +29 \end{array}$	**2.** $\begin{array}{r} 16 \\ +35 \end{array}$	**3.** $\begin{array}{r} 25 \\ +35 \end{array}$	**4.** $\begin{array}{r} 29 \\ +24 \end{array}$	**5.** $\begin{array}{r} 36 \\ +14 \end{array}$	**6.** $\begin{array}{r} 72 \\ +19 \end{array}$
7. $\begin{array}{r} 11 \\ 72 \\ +18 \end{array}$	**8.** $\begin{array}{r} 21 \\ 63 \\ +18 \end{array}$	**9.** $\begin{array}{r} 12 \\ 28 \\ +26 \end{array}$	**10.** $\begin{array}{r} 31 \\ 47 \\ +23 \end{array}$	**11.** $\begin{array}{r} 42 \\ 66 \\ +14 \end{array}$	**12.** $\begin{array}{r} 11 \\ 49 \\ +27 \end{array}$

13. $86 + 7 =$ _____   **14.** $75 + 8 =$ _____   **15.** $26 + 6 =$ _____   **16.** $55 + 9 =$ _____

17. $26 + 38 =$ _____   **18.** $57 + 23 =$ _____   **19.** $64 + 28 =$ _____   **20.** $39 + 12 =$ _____

Solve.

21. John's blue notebook has 35 extra pages. His red notebook has 37 extra pages. How many extra pages does he have altogether? _____

22. Joan has 18 books about animals. She has 15 books about people. How many more books does she have about animals?

_____

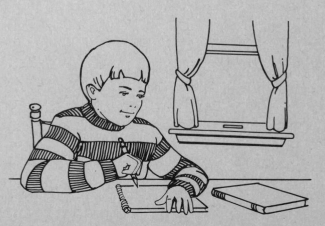

Practice

Student Book pp. 38–39

2-2

Estimate this sum.

$$46 \longrightarrow 50$$
$$82 \longrightarrow 80$$
$$\underline{+19} \longrightarrow \underline{+20}$$
$$150$$

To estimate sums, round each addend to its greatest place value. Then add the rounded numbers.

Estimate the sum.

1. 74 + 87	**2.** 38 + 28	**3.** 62 + 31	**4.** 54 + 28	**5.** 12 + 35	**6.** 35 + 18
7. 93 + 24	**8.** 48 + 23	**9.** 76 + 28	**10.** 29 + 46	**11.** 70 + 32	**12.** 64 + 26
13. 35 23 + 36	**14.** 42 36 + 14	**15.** 65 61 + 11	**16.** 24 73 + 32	**17.** 18 17 + 21	**18.** 14 5 + 22
19. 16 21 + 32	**20.** 25 26 + 31	**21.** 49 32 + 15	**22.** 31 42 + 10	**23.** 38 41 + 17	**24.** 12 11 + 9

Can you estimate the answer? Write *exact* or *estimate* to describe the numbers you would use. Then solve.

25. Paula has spaces in her photo album for 100 pictures. She has 42 pictures from her vacation. From a school field trip, she has 51 pictures. Is there enough space in her photo album for these pictures? _____

26. Jake needs 80 marbles to play a game. He has 26. A friend has promised to give him 53. Will he have enough marbles to play the game?

_____

Practice
Student Book pp. 40–41

Add 294 and 327.

Add the ones.	Add the tens.	Add the hundreds.
Rename 11 ones as 1 ten 1 one.	Rename 12 tens as 1 hundred 2 tens.	
1	11	11
294	294	294
+ 327	+ 327	+ 327
1	21	621

Add.

1.	175	2.	284	3.	297	4.	375	5.	329	6.	295
	+ 226		+ 176		+ 244		+ 268		+ 186		+ 124

7.	307	8.	198	9.	326	10.	458	11.	329	12.	458
	+ 256		+ 198		+ 85		+ 271		+ 116		+ 67

13.	141	14.	114	15.	693	16.	728	17.	654	18.	123
	257		726		46		210		31		881
	+ 338		+ 175		+ 241		+ 146		+ 206		+ 27

19. 647 + 228 = _____   20. 696 + 135 = _____   21. 443 + 278 = _____

22. 285 + 127 = _____   23. 495 + 156 = _____   24. 197 + 238 = _____

Solve.

25. Pat has 294 green stamps in his album. He has 316 blue stamps. How many stamps does he have altogether?

_____

26. Pat's sister, Sue, gave him 15 stamps for his birthday. Of the 15 new stamps, 6 were from France. The rest were from China. How many new stamps were from China?

_____

Practice
Student Book pp. 42–43

Add 3254 and 2936.

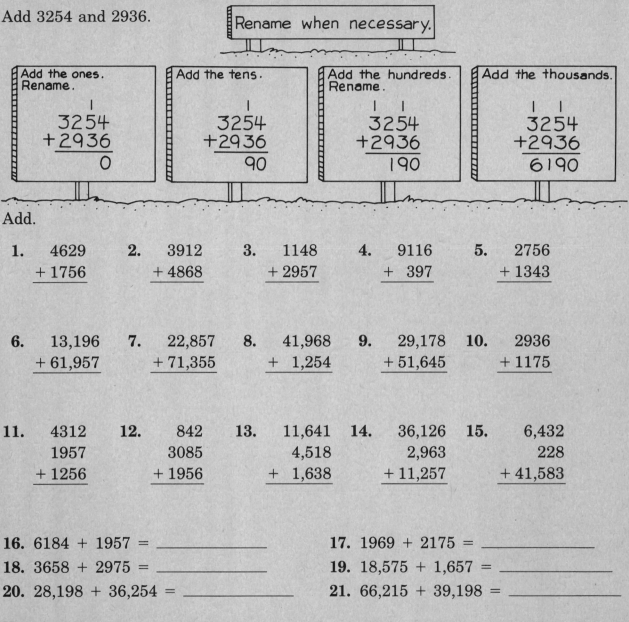

Rename when necessary.

Add the ones.
Rename.

$$3254$$
$$+2936$$
$$\overline{0}$$

Add the tens.

$$3254$$
$$+2936$$
$$\overline{90}$$

Add the hundreds.
Rename.

$$3254$$
$$+2936$$
$$\overline{190}$$

Add the thousands.

$$3254$$
$$+2936$$
$$\overline{6190}$$

Add.

1.	2.	3.	4.	5.
4629	3912	1148	9116	2756
+ 1756	+ 4868	+ 2957	+ 397	+ 1343

6.	7.	8.	9.	10.
13,196	22,857	41,968	29,178	2936
+ 61,957	+ 71,355	+ 1,254	+ 51,645	+ 1175

11.	12.	13.	14.	15.
4312	842	11,641	36,126	6,432
1957	3085	4,518	2,963	228
+ 1256	+ 1956	+ 1,638	+ 11,257	+ 41,583

16. 6184 + 1957 = _____   17. 1969 + 2175 = _____

18. 3658 + 2975 = _____   19. 18,575 + 1,657 = _____

20. 28,198 + 36,254 = _____   21. 66,215 + 39,198 = _____

Use the chart to estimate the answers to these problems. Round each number to the greatest place value. Then tell whether the actual sum will be *less than* or *greater than* the estimate.

Number of Miles Driven	
Mr. Robinson	12,586
Ms. Smith	13,857
Mr. Hernandez	20,998

22. About how many miles did Mr. Robinson and Ms. Smith drive altogether?

_____

23. About how many miles did Mr. Hernandez and Ms. Smith drive altogether?

_____

Name _____

Martina's Circus has 46 elephants that perform in the show. It has 18 elephants in training to perform. How many elephants does it have in all? To find how many elephants in all, add.

$$\begin{array}{r} 46 \\ +18 \\ \hline 54 \end{array}$$

Is the answer reasonable? Estimate to check.

$$50 + 20 = 70$$

The estimate and the sum are not close. The answer is not reasonable. Add again to find the error.

$$46 + 18 = 64$$

There are 64 elephants in all.

If the answer is reasonable, write *reasonable*. If the answer is not reasonable, give the correct answer.

1. Saturday's attendance was 1954 people. On Sunday, 2136 people came. How many people came altogether?

   Answer: 3090 people _____

2. The snack bar sold 624 cartons of juice during Saturday's afternoon performance. During the evening performance 487 cartons were sold. How many cartons were sold on Saturday?

   Answer: 1111 cartons _____

3. The circus has 64 elephants, 21 tigers, and 12 trained horses. How many animals are there altogether?

   Answer: 107 animals _____

4. The circus traveled 1160 miles last month. This month it has traveled 2880 miles. How many miles did it travel during these two months?

   Answer: 1720 miles _____

5. The circus has 231 workers to sell tickets and refreshments, and to help the performers. It has 96 performers. How many people in all work to put on a performance?

   Answer: 327 people _____

Practice

Student Book pp. 46–47

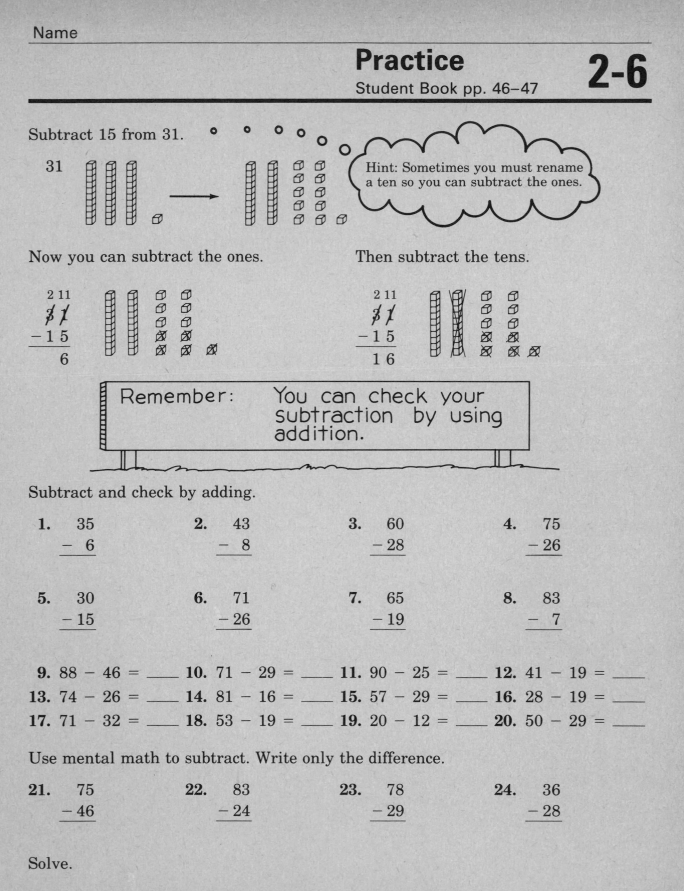

Subtract 15 from 31.

31

Hint: Sometimes you must rename a ten so you can subtract the ones.

Now you can subtract the ones.

Then subtract the tens.

2 11
3̸1̸
− 1 5
6

2 11
3̸1̸
− 1 5
1 6

Remember: You can check your subtraction by using addition.

Subtract and check by adding.

1. 35 − 6	**2.** 43 − 8	**3.** 60 − 28	**4.** 75 − 26
5. 30 − 15	**6.** 71 − 26	**7.** 65 − 19	**8.** 83 − 7

9. 88 − 46 = ____ **10.** 71 − 29 = ____ **11.** 90 − 25 = ____ **12.** 41 − 19 = ____

13. 74 − 26 = ____ **14.** 81 − 16 = ____ **15.** 57 − 29 = ____ **16.** 28 − 19 = ____

17. 71 − 32 = ____ **18.** 53 − 19 = ____ **19.** 20 − 12 = ____ **20.** 50 − 29 = ____

Use mental math to subtract. Write only the difference.

21. 75 − 46	**22.** 83 − 24	**23.** 78 − 29	**24.** 36 − 28

Solve.

25. Pal's Pet Center sold 24 dogs in June. In July, 36 dogs were sold. How many more dogs were sold in July? _____

Name _____

Estimate this difference.

$$46 \longrightarrow 50$$
$$-21 \longrightarrow -20$$
$$\overline{30}$$

To estimate differences, round each number to its greatest place value. Then subtract the rounded numbers.

Estimate the difference.

1.	76 −26	**2.**	38 −17	**3.**	42 −15	**4.**	76 −39	**5.**	58 −37	**6.**	31 −12
7.	92 −13	**8.**	86 −21	**9.**	82 −29	**10.**	66 −39	**11.**	72 −56	**12.**	48 − 9

13. 87 − 42 _____   **14.** 32 − 28 _____   **15.** 49 − 13 _____

16. 24 − 11 _____   **17.** 57 − 19 _____   **18.** 48 − 32 _____

Is the difference given reasonable? Estimate to find out. Write *yes* or *no*.

19.	46 −19 ‾‾ 27 _____	**20.**	82 −33 ‾‾ 39 _____	**21.**	67 −28 ‾‾ 49 _____	**22.**	86 −57 ‾‾ 29 _____
23.	46 −11 ‾‾ 25 _____	**24.**	70 −32 ‾‾ 48 _____	**25.**	26 −12 ‾‾ 38 _____	**26.**	65 −26 ‾‾ 39 _____

Estimate to complete this cross number puzzle. Watch the signs.

Across

a. 86 − 57
b. 61 + 32 + 41
d. 92 − 78
e. 81 + 26
h. 86 + 25
i. 48 − 36

Down

a. 51 − 20
b. 56 + 21 + 32
c. 78 − 49
f. 31 + 29 + 41
g. 86 − 25

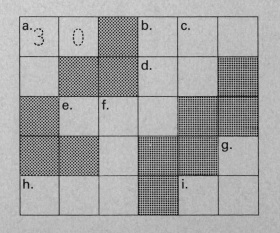

Practice

Student Book pp. 50–51

Subtract 229 from 427.

Rename 2 tens 7 ones as 1 ten 17 ones.	Subtract the ones.
1 17 4 2̸ 7̸ − 2 2 9	1 17 4 2̸ 7̸ − 2 2 9 ___ 8

Rename 4 hundreds 1 ten as 3 hundreds 11 tens.	Subtract the tens and hundreds.
11 3 4̸ 17 4̸ 2̸ 7̸ − 2 2 9 ___ 8	11 3 4̸ 17 4̸ 2̸ 7̸ − 2 2 9 ___ 1 9 8

Subtract.

1.	851 − 297	2.	913 − 256	3.	831 − 452	4.	724 − 106

5.	488 − 183	6.	521 − 342	7.	783 − 405	8.	842 − 296

9.	316 − 195	10.	472 − 193	11.	521 − 395	12.	615 − 46

Use mental math to subtract. Write only the difference.

13. $45 - 31 = $ _____   **14.** $67 - 25 = $ _____   **15.** $98 - 34 = $ _____

16. $846 - 226 = $ _____   **17.** $325 - 114 = $ _____   **18.** $795 - 254 = $ _____

Solve.

19. There were 414 books in the school library. On Monday, 295 books were checked out. How many books were left? _____

20. When the library opened, there were 552 books in the library. During the day, 125 books were checked out and 114 books were returned. When the library closed, were there more or fewer books than at the beginning of the day? _____

Practice

Student Book pp. 52–53

2-9

There were 400 runners at the start of the marathon race. Only 236 of them crossed the finish line. To find out how many runners didn't finish, we subtract.

Think of 400 as 40 tens. Rename 40 tens as 39 tens and 10 ones. Subtract.

```
 3 9 10              3 9 10
  4̸0̸0̸                 4̸0̸0̸
 − 236              − 236
                      164
```

There were 164 runners who didn't finish the race.

Subtract.

1. 305 − 196	**2.** 308 − 219	**3.** 605 − 427	**4.** 900 − 215	**5.** 806 − 225
6. 700 − 225	**7.** 300 − 27	**8.** 208 − 138	**9.** 405 − 97	**10.** 300 − 287
11. 400 − 246	**12.** 301 − 254	**13.** 604 − 205	**14.** 709 − 29	**15.** 600 − 152
16. 800 − 214	**17.** 905 − 541	**18.** 400 − 143	**19.** 309 − 129	**20.** 200 − 161

21. 600 − 415 = _____   **22.** 309 − 197 = _____   **23.** 200 − 163 = _____

24. 400 − 214 = _____   **25.** 101 − 93 = _____   **26.** 804 − 125 = _____

27. 900 − 241 = _____   **28.** 300 − 291 = _____   **29.** 305 − 125 = _____

Practice

Student Book pp. 54–55

Suppose the letters of the alphabet were worth points.

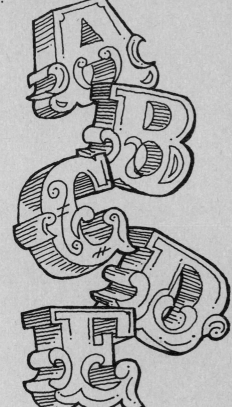

A = 5000	J = 1417	S = 3814
B = 2929	K = 4444	T = 1998
C = 1999	L = 575	U = 2000
D = 2910	M = 1390	V = 4612
E = 2500	N = 3777	W = 1416
F = 2416	O = 4000	X = 8888
G = 8912	P = 2327	Y = 1686
H = 5612	Q = 5555	Z = 7777
I = 4500	R = 4904	

Use the numbers above to write a subtraction problem for each word. Find each difference.

Here's how.

$$
\begin{array}{ll}
\text{BY} & B = 2929 \\
& -Y = 1686 \\
\hline
& 1243
\end{array}
$$

1. AT

2. GO

3. ON

4. IN

5. OF

6. AS

7. IS

8. BE

9. AN

10. IF

11. HI

12. IT

Practice

Student Book pp. 56–57

To write the value of an amount of money, you can use a cent sign or you can use a dollar sign and a decimal point.

2 dollars and 50 cents	250¢ or $2.50
four cents	4¢ or $ .04

Use a dollar sign and a decimal point to write the value.

1. 1 dollar 1 nickel _____

2. 172¢ _____

3. 1 dime 6 pennies _____

4. 1 dollar 2 quarters _____

5. 1 quarter 1 dime _____

6. 325¢ _____

7. 1 nickel 2 pennies _____

8. 2 dimes 8 pennies _____

9. 541¢ _____

10. 1 half dollar 3 dimes _____

11. 2 quarters 3 nickels _____

12. 3 dollars _____

13. 36¢ _____

14. 2 dollars 1 half dollar _____

15. 5 dollars _____

16. 874¢ _____

17. 10 dollars 1 quarter 2 nickels _____

18. 16 dollars 9 pennies _____

19. 2 dollars 1 half dollar 4 dimes _____

20. 409¢ _____

21. 17 dollars 4 dimes 1 penny _____

22. 15 dollars 1 half dollar 2 nickels _____

Which amount is greater? Write *a* or *b*, then use a dollar sign and a decimal point to write the greater value.

23. a. 6 dimes   3 nickels   4 pennies
     b. 2 quarters   2 dimes   2 nickels   1 penny   _____

24. a. 3 dimes   4 nickels   6 pennies
     b. 1 quarter   3 nickels   7 pennies   _____

25. a. 4 dollars   6 dimes   3 nickels
     b. 4 dollars   1 half dollar   1 quarter   2 pennies   _____

26. a. 5 dollars   3 quarters   6 dimes
     b. 5 dollars   1 half dollar   2 quarters   8 nickels   _____

Practice

Student Book pp. 58–59

What is the cost of the hat and
the scarf?

```
        1
  $ 5.19
  +  8.76
  $13.95    The cost is $13.95.
```
Keep decimal points in line.

Carmelita bought the hat and the
scarf. She gave the clerk $15.00. How
much change did the clerk give her?

```
      4 9 10
  $15.00
  − 13.95
  $ 1.05    Her change was $1.05.
```

Add or subtract.

1. $ .75 + .40	**2.** $ 2.47 − .68	**3.** $ 5.35 − .79	**4.** $ 3.99 + 2.56	**5.** $ 2.18 + 5.79
6. $ 4.66 + 3.14	**7.** $10.00 + 12.99	**8.** $ 8.32 + 7.65	**9.** $ 6.75 − 2.43	**10.** $ 7.05 − 3.59
11. $19.04 − 5.98	**12.** $42.99 − 31.99	**13.** $36.25 − 14.72	**14.** $27.88 + 16.54	**15.** $18.39 − 10.68
16. $ 2.06 .76 + 3.96	**17.** $ 3.54 1.98 + 2.94	**18.** $10.99 4.25 + 5.15	**19.** $17.85 15.75 + 4.12	**20.** $12.76 16.57 + 11.27

Estimate. Is the savings *greater than* or *less than* $1.00?

21. original price: $6.49
     sale price: $5.77 _____

22. original price: $2.98
     sale price: $2.06 _____

23. original price: $14.95
     sale price: $13.66 _____

24. original price: $12.50
     sale price: $11.29 _____

Practice

Student Book pp. 60–61

2-13

You can find the coins and bills needed for change by counting it out. Start with the price of the item and count to the amount you were given. Assemble the coins as you count. Always try to use the fewest coins and bills possible.

Amount of Purchase	Amount Given	Change			
$13.69	$15.00				
	Count:	$13.70	$13.75	$14.00	$15.00

You give 1 penny, 1 nickel, 1 quarter, and 1 one-dollar bill. The change is $1.31.

Solve. When finding the change use the fewest coins and bills possible.

1. Sam bought a new baseball for $3.21 including tax. He gave the clerk a five-dollar bill. What coins and bill does the clerk give Sam for his change?

_____

2. Jennifer gave a clerk a ten-dollar bill to pay for lunch. The amount of her lunch check was $3.48. What coins and bills does the clerk give Jennifer for her change?

_____

3. Matthew received 3 pennies, 1 dime, one quarter and 2 one-dollar bills as change. He gave the clerk a ten-dollar bill for an $8.62 purchase. Did he receive the correct change? If your answer is no, explain.

_____

4. LuAnn bought a pencil for 51¢. She gave the clerk a one-dollar bill. How can the clerk make the change if there are no dimes left in the cash register?

_____

5. Peg gave the cashier $20 to buy a record that cost $11.66. She received 4 pennies, 1 quarter, 3 one-dollar bills, and 1 five-dollar bill as change. Did Peg receive the correct change? If your answer is no, explain.

_____

March						
S	**M**	**T**	**W**	**T**	**F**	**S**
		1	2	3	4	5
6	7	8	9	10	11	12
13	14	15	16	17	18	19
20	21	22	23	24	25	26
27	28	29	30	31		

Use the calendar above. Write the date.

1. the second Tuesday _____
2. the fifth Wednesday _____
3. the fourth Friday _____
4. three days after the third Sunday _____
5. four days before the second Monday _____
6. five days after the third Saturday _____
7. ten days after the second Wednesday _____

Use the calendar above. Write the day of the week.

8. March 31 _____   9. March 1 _____
10. March 22 _____   11. March 18 _____
12. ten days after Tuesday, March 8 _____
13. fifteen days before Monday, March 28 _____

Solve. Use the calendar above.

14. Jan takes gymnastics lessons every Tuesday. How many lessons will she have in March?

_____

15. Matt is going to the zoo on March 27. Today is March 22. How many days is it until he goes to the zoo? _____

Practice

Student Book pp. 72–73

Complete to show how to read the time shown. Then write the time.

1.

_____ minutes

after _____

_____ : _____

2.

_____ minutes

after _____

_____ : _____

3.

_____ minutes

after _____

_____ : _____

4.

_____ minutes

before _____

_____ : _____

5.

_____ minutes

before _____

_____ : _____

6.

`6:35`

_____ minutes

before _____

_____ : _____

Solve.

7. Kay must be at a meeting at 15 minutes before 2. She walks past a bank clock on the way to the meeting. The clock shows the time 1:35. Is she late for the meeting? _____

8. Mary arrived at the meeting at a quarter to two. Kay arrived at 1:40. Who arrived first?

_____

9. The meeting was scheduled to end at 2:45. It ended at 10 minutes before 3. Did it end early, on time, or late? _____

When you add or subtract time you sometimes need to rename hours, minutes, or seconds.

Add the seconds. Rename. Add the minutes.

$$\begin{array}{r} 1 \\ 4 \text{ minutes } 54 \text{ seconds} \\ + 2 \text{ minutes } 32 \text{ seconds} \\ \hline 7 \text{ minutes } 26 \text{ seconds} \end{array}$$

Think: 86 seconds is 1 minute 26 seconds

Rename 1 hour. Subtract minutes. Subtract hours.

$$\begin{array}{r} 6 \quad 86 \\ \cancel{7} \text{ hours } \cancel{26} \text{ minutes} \\ - 2 \text{ hours } 32 \text{ minutes} \\ \hline 4 \text{ hours } 54 \text{ minutes} \end{array}$$

Think: 1 hour = 60 minutes. 60 + 26 = 86

Add or subtract.

1. $\begin{array}{r} 1 \text{ hour } 24 \text{ minutes} \\ + 1 \text{ hour } 16 \text{ minutes} \\ \hline \end{array}$

2. $\begin{array}{r} 4 \text{ minutes } 48 \text{ seconds} \\ - 2 \text{ minutes } 32 \text{ seconds} \\ \hline \end{array}$

3. $\begin{array}{r} 3 \text{ hours } 45 \text{ minutes} \\ + 2 \text{ hours } 32 \text{ minutes} \\ \hline \end{array}$

4. $\begin{array}{r} 3 \text{ hour } 3 \text{ minutes} \\ - 1 \text{ hour } 29 \text{ minutes} \\ \hline \end{array}$

5. $\begin{array}{r} 1 \text{ minute } 56 \text{ seconds} \\ + 1 \text{ minute } 14 \text{ seconds} \\ \hline \end{array}$

6. $\begin{array}{r} 2 \text{ hours } 48 \text{ minutes} \\ + 1 \text{ hour } 15 \text{ minutes} \\ \hline \end{array}$

7. $\begin{array}{r} 8 \text{ hours } 18 \text{ minutes} \\ - 6 \text{ hours } 32 \text{ minutes} \\ \hline \end{array}$

8. $\begin{array}{r} 6 \text{ minutes } 12 \text{ seconds} \\ - 2 \text{ minutes } 45 \text{ seconds} \\ \hline \end{array}$

9. $\begin{array}{r} 4 \text{ hours } 48 \text{ minutes} \\ + 2 \text{ hours } 45 \text{ minutes} \\ \hline \end{array}$

10. $\begin{array}{r} 9 \text{ minutes } 48 \text{ seconds} \\ - 2 \text{ minutes } 54 \text{ seconds} \\ \hline \end{array}$

11. $\begin{array}{r} 2 \text{ minutes } 28 \text{ seconds} \\ + 1 \text{ minute } 12 \text{ seconds} \\ \hline \end{array}$

12. $\begin{array}{r} 6 \text{ hours } 45 \text{ minutes} \\ - 4 \text{ hours } 35 \text{ minutes} \\ \hline \end{array}$

Solve.

13. Dad cooks his special spaghetti sauce for 3 hours 30 minutes. Mom cooks her sauce 45 minutes longer than Dad. How long does she cook her spaghetti sauce? _____

14. Mom completed the grocery shopping in 1 hour 45 minutes. Last week Dad completed the grocery shopping in 2 hours 10 minutes. How much longer did it take Dad to shop for groceries? _____

Martha leaves for basketball practice at 3:30 P.M.
She returns at 5:00 P.M. How long is she gone?

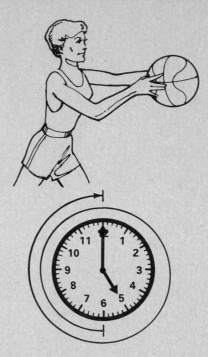

Subtract to solve.

5:00 P.M.

3:30 P.M.

$$\begin{array}{r} \overset{4}{\cancel{5}} \text{ hours } \overset{60}{\cancel{0}} \text{ minutes} \\ - 3 \text{ hours } 30 \text{ minutes} \\ \hline 1 \text{ hour } 30 \text{ minutes} \end{array}$$

She is gone for 1 hour and 30 minutes.

To check your answer, you can count on a clock.
3:30 P.M. to 4:30 P.M. is 1 hour.
4:30 P.M. to 5:00 P.M. is 30 minutes.
So 3:30 P.M. to 5:00 P.M. is 1 hour 30 minutes.

Solve. Check your answer by counting on a clock.

1. You leave at 9:15 A.M. You return at 10:00 A.M. How long
   are you gone? _____

2. You get on a bus at 3:20 P.M. You get off at 10:00 P.M. How
   long was the trip? _____

3. Bob works at the library on Saturday mornings. He arrives
   at 8:00 A.M. and leaves at 11:45 A.M. How long does he
   work? _____

4. School starts at 8:00 A.M. The earliest students may enter
   the school is 15 minutes before school starts. What is the
   earliest time students may enter the school? _____

5. You want to be at school early on Monday. It takes you 45
   minutes to get to school and 30 minutes to get ready for
   school. What time must you get up to get to school at 7:30
   A.M.? _____

6. Jose gets up at 8:00 A.M. on Saturdays. It takes him 45
   minutes to eat and get dressed. He cleans his room for 1
   hour and helps his father do yard work for another hour. He
   may then play with his friends. What time does he play
   with his friends? _____

Name _____

A centimeter (cm) is a metric unit of length.

The length of the toothbrush is between 14 cm and 15 cm. It is nearer 15 cm. The length of the toothbrush to the nearest centimeter is 15 cm.

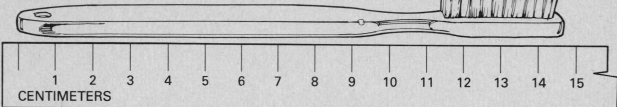

The length of the comb is between 8 cm and 9 cm. The length of the comb to the nearest centimeter is 9 cm.

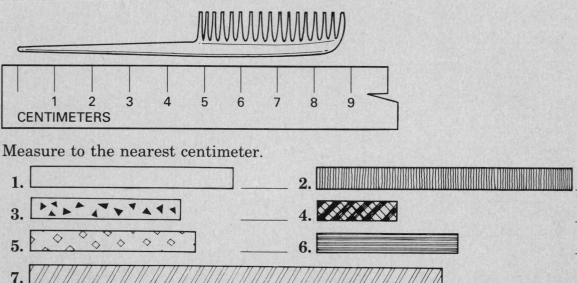

Measure to the nearest centimeter.

1. _____ _____   2. _____ _____

3. _____ _____   4. _____ _____

5. _____ _____   6. _____ _____

7. _____ _____

8. _____ _____

Without a ruler estimate the length of each pencil. Then measure to the nearest centimeter to check your estimate.

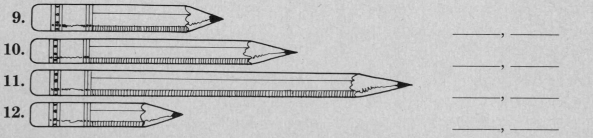

9. _____ , _____

10. _____ , _____

11. _____ , _____

12. _____ , _____

Is the estimate reasonable? Write *yes* or *no*.

13. The width of your hand is about 12 cm. _____

14. The length of this worksheet is between 25 cm and 30 cm. _____

Practice
Student Book pp. 80–81

3-6

Centimeters are used to measure short lengths. The width of your fingernail is about a centimeter.

Meters (m) are used to measure long lengths. The distance from the floor to the top of a kitchen stove is about a meter.

$$1 \text{ meter} = 100 \text{ centimeters} \qquad 1 \text{ m} = 100 \text{ cm}$$

Kilometers (km) are used to measure longer distances. If you ran around a baseball diamond nine times, you would have run about a kilometer.

$$1 \text{ kilometer} = 1000 \text{ meters} \qquad 1 \text{ km} = 1000 \text{ m}$$

Ring the better estimate.

1. length of a pen
   14 cm   14 m

2. length of a teaspoon
   15 cm   15 m

3. height of a basketball player
   2 cm   2 m

4. width of a table
   1 m   1 km

5. width of a math book
   14 m   14 cm

6. length of a caterpillar
   5 m   5 cm

7. length of a chopstick
   25 cm   25 m

8. distance of a train trip
   40 m   40 km

9. length of a canoe
   4 km   4 m

10. length of a hammer
    30 cm   30 m

11. height of a giraffe
    4 km   4 m

12. thickness of a dictionary
    5 cm   5 m

13. distance of a car trip
    50 km   50 m

14. length of a theater
    25 m   25 km

Use the signs to answer.

15. How far is it from Manchester to Lakeview?

    _____

16. How much farther is it from Manchester to Lakeview than from Manchester to Springfield?

    _____

Name _____

Practice
Student Book pp. 82–83

3-7

We use grams (g) to measure the mass of light objects. The marigold seeds in one packet have a mass of about one gram.

We use kilograms to measure the mass of heavier objects. A bag of soil weighs about one kilogram.

1 kg = 1000 g

Ring the better estimate.

1. a safety pin
1 g   1 kg

2. a bag of flour
2 kg   2 g

3. a stack of newspapers
5 kg   5 g

4. a cake of soap
100 kg   100 g

5. a turkey
8 g   8 kg

6. a jar of peanut butter
500 kg   500 g

7. a pair of boots
2 g   2 kg

8. a handful of feathers
4 kg   4 g

9. a tube of toothpaste
200 kg   200 g

10. a loaf of bread
400 kg   400 g

11. a tennis racquet
1 g   1 kg

12. a piece of chalk
15 g   15 kg

13. a large dog
25 g   25 kg

14. a watermelon
7 g   7 kg

15. a ten year old
35 g   35 kg

16. a postcard
15 kg   15 g

17. a newborn baby
3 kg   3 g

18. a hairbrush
70 kg   70 g

Solve.

19. Ms. Brown went to the nursery to buy soil for her flower bed. She bought two 18-kg bags of top soil. How many kilograms of top soil did she buy in all? _____

20. Mr. Chin bought three small bags of different types of grass seed. The total mass of the three bags was 1264 g. Is this more or less than a kilogram? _____

Practice
Student Book pp. 84–85

3-8

We use milliliters (mL) to measure small amounts.

Mrs. Wang uses an eyedropper to feed the newborn kitten. The eyedropper holds about 1 milliliter of milk.

We use liters (L) to measure greater amounts of liquid.

Billy Wang pours milk for his family. The bottle holds about 1 liter.

1000 mL = 1 L

Choose the better unit for measuring. Write mL or L.

1. milk in a glass _____

2. water in a bucket _____

3. water in a bathtub _____

4. soup in a cup _____

5. milk in a thermos _____

6. soup in a bowl _____

7. cough syrup in a spoon _____

8. a large carton of milk _____

9. a drink for a parakeet _____

10. a drink for an elephant _____

11. orange juice in a pitcher _____

12. perfume in a bottle _____

13. ink in a bottle _____

14. gas for a car _____

Use the facts below. Count by hundreds or thousands to complete.

1000 mL = 1 L   1000 g = 1 kg   100 cm = 1 m

15. 6 L = _____ mL

16. 8 m = _____ cm

17. 4 kg = _____ g

18. 5 L = _____ mL

Solve.

19. Mr. White Feather has a 450-mL can of oil. He also has a 500-mL can of oil. He needs a liter of oil. Does he have enough?

_____

20. One glass holds 250 mL. Another glass holds 400 mL, and a third glass holds 350 mL. How much milk is needed to fill the three glasses? _____

Practice

3-9

Write the temperature for each letter in the picture.

1. A _____   2. B _____   3. C _____   4. D _____

5. E _____   6. F _____   7. G _____   8. H _____

Write the letter to match the temperature and the situation.

9. 100°C _____   W fall day

10. 15°C _____   X person with a fever

11. 39°C _____   Y boiling eggs

12. ⁻10°C _____   Z skating on a pond

Write *add* or *subtract* for your plan. Then solve.

13. The temperature for baking a cake is 180°C. The temperature for baking a pie is 210°C. What's the difference between these temperatures?

   _____

14. Normal body temperature is 37°C. When Derek was ill, his temperature went up 3°C. What was his temperature when he was ill?

   _____

15. The temperature outside is 15°C. Tonight the temperature is expected to drop 10°C. What will the temperature be then?

   _____

16. The temperature this morning was 16°C. By 2:00 P.M. it was 14°C warmer. What was the temperature at 2:00 P.M.?

   _____

Practice

The inch (in.), the foot (ft), the yard (yd), and the mile (mi) are United States units used to measure length.

This pencil is about 5 in. long.

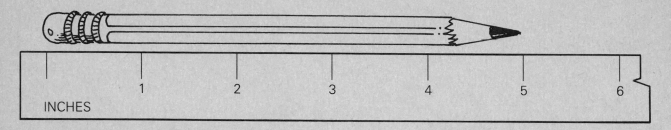

A looseleaf binder is about 1 ft long.
  1 ft = 12 in.

The Grand Canyon is about 1 mi deep.
  1 mi = 5280 ft   1 mi = 1760 yd

Brenda's camp trunk is about 1 yd wide.
  1 yd = 3 ft

Ring the better estimate.

1. length of a crayon
   3 in.   3 ft

2. distance between two cities
   26 yd   26 mi

3. width of a table
   4 ft   4 mi

4. length of a bus trip
   100 mi   100 ft

5. length of a spoon
   5 in.   5 ft

6. height of an oak tree
   30 ft   30 in.

7. length of a mouse
   3 yd   3 in.

8. length of a bench
   10 in.   10 ft

9. length of a field
   600 mi   600 yd

Complete.

10. 1 ft 6 in. = _____ in.

11. 2 ft = _____ in.

12. 2 yd = _____ ft

13. 3 ft = _____ in.

14. 3 yd = _____ ft

15. 4 ft = _____ in.

Solve.

16. The length of a jump rope is 2 yd. How many feet is that? _____

17. Maria has 39 in. of wire. She needs 1 yd. Does she have enough? _____

Practice

The cup (c), the pint (pt), the quart (qt), and the gallon (gal) are United States units used to measure liquids.

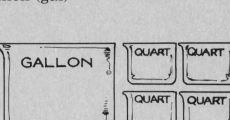
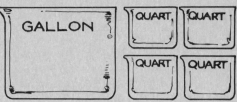

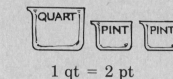

1 pt = 2 c   1 qt = 2 pt   1 gal = 4 qt

The ounce (oz), the pound (lb), and the ton (t) are United States units used to measure weight.

The wedge of cheese weighs 1 lb.
1 lb = 16 oz

A young elephant weighs 1 t.
1 t = 2000 lb

Ring the better estimate.

1. juice in a glass
   1 qt   1 c

2. weight of an apple
   10 oz   10 t

3. car gas tank
   15 gal   15 c

4. flour in a bowl
   6 t   6 oz

5. milk in a jug
   1 gal   1 c

6. carton of juice
   2 qt   2 gal

7. cheese in a sandwich
   1 lb   1 oz

8. weight of a tiger
   815 lb   815 oz

9. yogurt in a cup
   8 oz   8 lb

Compare the measures. Write < or > .

10. 1 t _____ 2500 lb

11. 1 lb _____ 12 oz

12. 20 oz _____ 1 lb

13. 1 pt _____ 1 qt

14. 3 qt _____ 1 gal

15. 4 c _____ 1 pt

16. 1000 lb _____ 1 t

17. 6 oz _____ 1 lb

18. 1 gal _____ 5 qt

Solve.

19. A punch recipe calls for 2 qt of orange juice, 2 pt of pineapple juice and 1 qt of cranberry juice. Will this recipe make 1 gal of punch? _____

20. A baby drank 3 oz of milk at 3 A.M. He drank 8 oz at 7 A.M. and 6 oz at 11 A.M. How much milk did he drink during the morning? _____

Sometimes you don't have all the facts you need to solve a problem. Match each problem with its missing fact. Write the letter. Then solve.

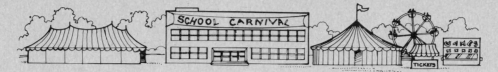

1. John bought 12 tickets to the school carnival. How many more tickets than Joan did he buy? _____

A. There were 25 tickets on a roll.

2. A clown gave away 265 balloons in the morning. How many balloons did the clown give away in all?

_____

B. There were 3 magic shows.

3. Fred has 5 more tickets than Carlos. How many tickets does Fred have? _____

C. Joan bought 8 tickets.

4. There was a magician at the carnival who put on magic shows. Each show lasted 15 minutes. How many minutes did the magician perform? _____

D. A glass of juice cost 30¢.

5. Marsha bought 1 glass of juice at the carnival. She gave the clerk 50¢. How much change did she get back? _____

E. There were 5 rabbits.

6. There was a pet judging contest at the carnival. There were 34 dogs and 23 cats entered in the contest. There were also some rabbits. Altogether, how many animals were in the contest? _____

F. She gave away 463 balloons in the afternoon and 161 balloons in the evening.

7. During the morning, Kim sold 2 rolls of tickets. How many tickets did she sell? _____

G. Carlos has 14 tickets.

Name _____

Practice

Student Book pp. 102–103

Each clover has 3 leaves.
How many leaves do 5 clovers have?
To find out, you can add.

$$3 + 3 + 3 + 3 + 3 = 15$$

5 threes equal 15.
You can also multiply.

Five times three equals fifteen.
There are 15 leaves on the five clovers.

Write a multiplication fact.

1. 4 + 4 + 4 + 4 + 4 _____   2. 4 + 4 + 4 _____
3. 4 + 4 _____   4. 2 + 2 + 2 + 2 _____
5. 6 fours _____   6. 9 fours _____   7. 9 twos _____
8. 4 threes _____   9. 3 twos _____   10. 7 threes _____

Use skip counting to find the answer. Write the product only.

11. 7×2 _____   12. 6×2 _____   13. 3×3 _____
14. 8×3 _____   15. 7×4 _____   16. 4×4 _____
17. 2×2 _____   18. 9×3 _____   19. 8×4 _____

Solve.

20. Carnations sell for $2 a bunch. The owner sold 5 bunches. How much money did he collect? _____

21. Each potted plant has 3 bows on it. There are 6 plants. How many bows in all? _____

22. Each daisy has 2 leaves. There are 8 daisies. How many leaves in all? _____

23. A customer needed 24 roses. The owner had 4 bunches of roses left. There were 6 roses in each bunch. Were there enough roses for the customer? _____

Practice
Student Book pp. 104–105

You can think of multiplication as repeated addition.

$2 + 2 + 2 = 6$
$3 \times 2 = 6$

$3 + 3 + 3 + 3 = 12$
$4 \times 3 = 12$

$4 + 4 + 4 + 4 = 16$
$4 \times 4 = 16$

Multiply.

1. $7 \times 2 =$ _____ **2.** $6 \times 4 =$ _____ **3.** $6 \times 3 =$ _____ **4.** $2 \times 2 =$ _____

5. $8 \times 4 =$ _____ **6.** $6 \times 2 =$ _____ **7.** $9 \times 4 =$ _____ **8.** $2 \times 4 =$ _____

9.	10.	11.	12.	13.	14.
2	4	4	3	3	3
×5	×4	×7	×9	×2	×3

15.	16.	17.	18.	19.	20.
3	4	2	3	2	3
×5	×3	×8	×7	×4	×8

Solve.

21. Nick borrowed a magazine from the library. It was due on November 2. He returned it on November 8. How much was his fine? _____

22. Magazines may be borrowed for 1 week. You borrowed a magazine on November 5. When is it due?

_____

Library Fines

Overdue Book	3¢ per day
Overdue Magazines	4¢ per day

November						
S	M	T	W	T	F	S
	1	2	3	4	5	6
7	8	9	10	11	12	13
14	15	16	17	18	19	20

Practice

Student Book pp. 106–107

There are 5 erasers in a package. The school store sold 9 packages. To find out how many erasers the store sold, multiply 9 × 5.

$9 \times 5 = 45$

The store sold 45 erasers.

multiplying fives

×	5
0	0
1	5
2	10
3	15
4	20
5	25
6	30
7	35
8	40
9	45

Multiply.

1. $8 \times 4 =$ _____   **2.** $6 \times 3 =$ _____   **3.** $7 \times 4 =$ _____   **4.** $2 \times 5 =$ _____

5. $1 \times 5 =$ _____   **6.** $7 \times 3 =$ _____   **7.** $8 \times 2 =$ _____   **8.** $9 \times 3 =$ _____

9. $9 \times 4 =$ _____   **10.** $8 \times 3 =$ _____   **11.** $1 \times 3 =$ _____   **12.** $7 \times 2 =$ _____

13. $4 \times 5 =$ _____   **14.** $7 \times 5 =$ _____   **15.** $2 \times 2 =$ _____   **16.** $9 \times 2 =$ _____

17.	18.	19.	20.	21.
$\begin{array}{r} 5 \\ \times 5 \\ \hline \end{array}$	$\begin{array}{r} 3 \\ \times 2 \\ \hline \end{array}$	$\begin{array}{r} 2 \\ \times 6 \\ \hline \end{array}$	$\begin{array}{r} 5 \\ \times 3 \\ \hline \end{array}$	$\begin{array}{r} 2 \\ \times 1 \\ \hline \end{array}$

22.	23.	24.	25.	26.
$\begin{array}{r} 4 \\ \times 6 \\ \hline \end{array}$	$\begin{array}{r} 3 \\ \times 3 \\ \hline \end{array}$	$\begin{array}{r} 3 \\ \times 4 \\ \hline \end{array}$	$\begin{array}{r} 2 \\ \times 4 \\ \hline \end{array}$	$\begin{array}{r} 5 \\ \times 8 \\ \hline \end{array}$

27.	28.	29.	30.	31.
$\begin{array}{r} 2 \\ \times 5 \\ \hline \end{array}$	$\begin{array}{r} 4 \\ \times 2 \\ \hline \end{array}$	$\begin{array}{r} 4 \\ \times 1 \\ \hline \end{array}$	$\begin{array}{r} 4 \\ \times 4 \\ \hline \end{array}$	$\begin{array}{r} 3 \\ \times 5 \\ \hline \end{array}$

Solve.

32. There are 5 pencils in each package. The school store sold 6 packages. How many pencils were sold? _____

33. The school store made a profit of $28 last week and $32 this week. What was the total profit for the two weeks? _____

Multiply. Then color the shapes that have a product less than 4.

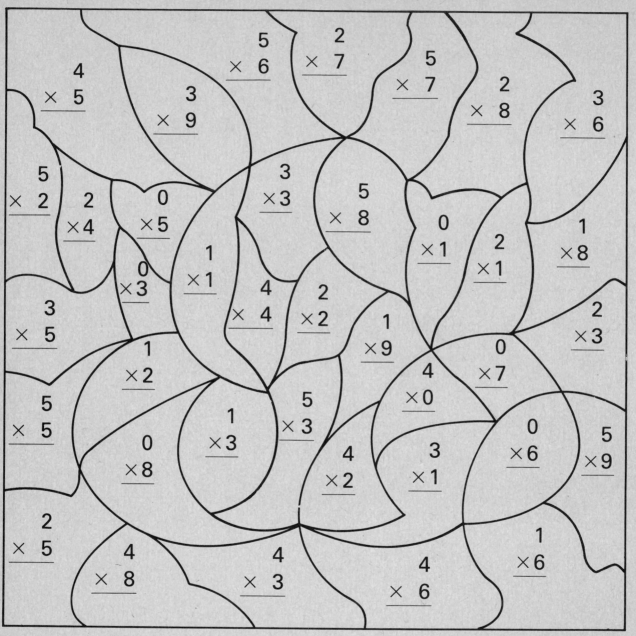

1. What did you find? _____

Write a number sentence. Solve.

2. There are 2 chipmunks gathering nuts. Each finds 4 nuts.
   How many nuts did they find? _____

3. One chipmunk ate 5 nuts. The other chipmunk ate 10 nuts.
   How many more nuts did the second chipmunk eat? _____

Name _____

You can think of 10 as 2 fives or 5 twos.

2 fives
$2 \times 5 = 10$ ● ● ● ● ●
                    ● ● ● ● ●

5 twos
$5 \times 2 = 10$ ● ●
                    ● ●
                    ● ●
                    ● ●
                    ● ●

Also, changing the grouping of the factors does not change the product.

$(3 \times 2) \times 4$ $3 \times (2 \times 4)$
$\ \ 6\ \ \ \times 4 = 24$ $3 \times\ \ \ 8 = 24$

Multiply.

1.   4   2.   3   3.   2   4.   1   5.   4   6.   5
    $\times 9$ $\times 8$ $\times 6$ $\times 9$ $\times 8$ $\times 7$

7.   9   8.   8   9.   6   10.   9   11.   8   12.   7
    $\times 4$ $\times 3$ $\times 2$ $\times 1$ $\times 4$ $\times 5$

13. $3 \times (2 \times 1) = $ _____   14. $(3 \times 2) \times 2 = $ _____   15. $3 \times (3 \times 2) = $ _____

Complete.

16. $4 \times 6 = $ _____   17. $5 \times 8 = $ _____   18. $(2 \times 4) \times 1 = $ _____
    $6 \times$ _____ $= 24$ _____ $\times 5 = 40$ _____ $\times (4 \times 1) = 8$

There were 6 puppies and 12 kittens at Pete's Pet Store. Each was on sale for $5 off the regular price.

Solve.

19. Pete wants to give each puppy 2 dog biscuits. How many dog biscuits does he need?

    _____

20. The regular price of a kitten is $20. How much is the sale price? _____

21. Pete sold a dog food dish and a cat food dish. What was the total cost of these two dishes?

    _____

Practice
Student Book pp. 112–113

Betty wants to buy either a toy truck or a toy car. Both come in three different colors, white, blue, and red. How many different toy cars or trucks does Betty have to choose from?

A tree diagram can be used to solve this problem.

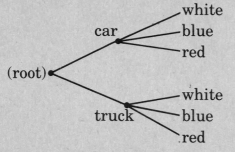

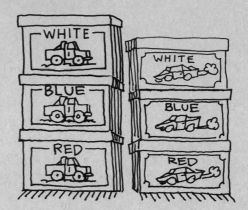

Betty has 6 different toys to choose from.

Draw a tree diagram. Solve.

1. Bob wants to ask one friend to stay over. He has three friends to choose from. Each friend can stay over on either Saturday or Sunday. How many different ways can he plan this visit? _____

2. Lazaro can serve his friend an apple, a pear, or an orange. He can put the piece of fruit on a plate, in a bowl, or on a napkin. How many different ways can he serve his friend? _____

3. Mei Su may watch one of 4 movies to be shown on TV this week. Each will be on 2 different days. How many different choices does she have? _____

Complete the multiplication charts.

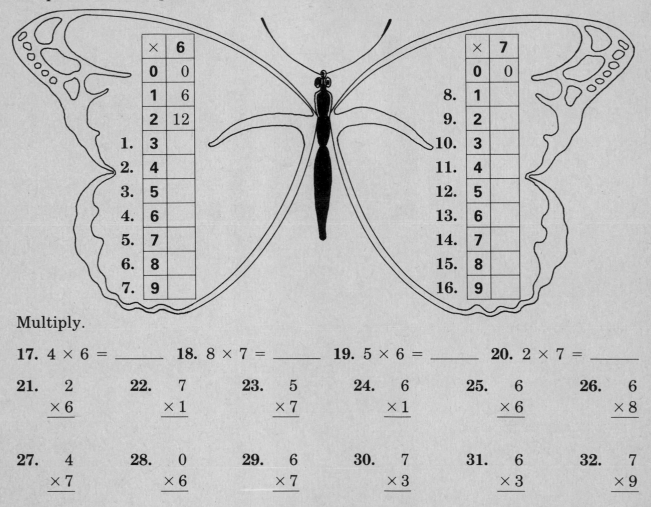

×	6
0	0
1	6
2	12
1. 3	
2. 4	
3. 5	
4. 6	
5. 7	
6. 8	
7. 9	

×	7
0	0
8. 1	
9. 2	
10. 3	
11. 4	
12. 5	
13. 6	
14. 7	
15. 8	
16. 9	

Multiply.

17. 4 × 6 = _____   **18.** 8 × 7 = _____   **19.** 5 × 6 = _____   **20.** 2 × 7 = _____

21. 2
   × 6

22. 7
   × 1

23. 5
   × 7

24. 6
   × 1

25. 6
   × 6

26. 6
   × 8

27. 4
   × 7

28. 0
   × 6

29. 6
   × 7

30. 7
   × 3

31. 6
   × 3

32. 7
   × 9

Three students perform at the piano recital. Each student plays the number of pieces shown. Each piece takes 6 minutes to play. Solve.

Piano Recital	
Student	**Pieces**
Jason Brown	2
Mary Chin	4
Matt Levitt	3

33. How long will it take Matt to perform his pieces?

_____

34. Whose performance will be the longest? How long will it be?

_____

35. To prepare for the recital, Mary plays each piece 5 times each day. How long does it take her to practice one piece?

_____

Practice
Student Book pp. 116–117

4-8

The truck has 8 wheels.
How many wheels are there on 9 trucks?

$9 \times 8 = 72$ wheels
There are 72 wheels on 9 trucks.

Multiply.

1. $8 \times 4 =$ _____   **2.** $8 \times 6 =$ _____   **3.** $9 \times 5 =$ _____   **4.** $9 \times 3 =$ _____

5. $8 \times 1 =$ _____   **6.** $9 \times 1 =$ _____   **7.** $8 \times 0 =$ _____   **8.** $9 \times 0 =$ _____

9. $6 \times 9 =$ _____   **10.** $5 \times 8 =$ _____   **11.** $8 \times 8 =$ _____   **12.** $9 \times 9 =$ _____

13. 9×4	**14.** 2×8	**15.** 8×3	**16.** 5×9	**17.** 6×8	**18.** 9×9
19. 3×9	**20.** 1×9	**21.** 8×5	**22.** 0×8	**23.** 8×7	**24.** 7×9
25. 4×8	**26.** 8×9	**27.** 9×7	**28.** 9×2	**29.** 7×8	**30.** 4×9

Solve.

31. The truck driver is delivering cartons of fresh fruit to 6 different supermarkets. He is delivering 9 cartons to each supermarket. How many cartons of fresh fruit is the driver delivering in all? _____

Practice

Student Book pp. 118–119

4-9

Multiply.

1. 4 × 4 = _____   2. 4 × 6 = _____   3. 6 × 7 = _____   4. 9 × 4 = _____
5. 6 × 8 = _____   6. 7 × 4 = _____   7. 5 × 5 = _____   8. 8 × 9 = _____
9. 5 × 6 = _____   10. 4 × 8 = _____   11. 0 × 3 = _____   12. 6 × 6 = _____

13.	14.	15.	16.	17.	18.
7 ×5	8 ×8	9 ×1	4 ×3	5 ×2	7 ×0

19.	20.	21.	22.	23.	24.
7 ×9	5 ×8	3 ×5	7 ×7	0 ×8	6 ×2

25.	26.	27.	28.	29.	30.
3 ×7	1 ×7	9 ×5	6 ×9	8 ×7	2 ×3

31.	32.	33.	34.	35.	36.
2 ×0	7 ×8	9 ×9	3 ×8	1 ×3	0 ×0

37.	38.	39.	40.	41.	42.
8 ×9	6 ×3	5 ×1	0 ×1	2 ×9	1 ×1

43.	44.	45.	46.	47.	48.
8 ×5	6 ×1	9 ×6	8 ×2	5 ×0	2 ×2

49.	50.	51.	52.	53.	54.
4 ×8	0 ×4	5 ×7	6 ×8	2 ×7	4 ×1

55.	56.	57.	58.	59.	60.
7 ×4	0 ×9	4 ×2	5 ×9	9 ×7	2 ×1

61.	62.	63.	64.	65.	66.
3 ×9	6 ×7	3 ×3	8 ×1	0 ×6	4 ×5

Practice

The multiplication charts show some of the *multiples* of 4 and some of the *multiples* of 6.

$5 \times 4 = 20$, so 20 is a *multiple* of 4.
$3 \times 6 = 18$, so 18 is a *multiple* of 6.

×	4
1	4
2	8
3	12
4	16
5	20
6	24
7	28
8	32
9	36

×	6
1	6
2	12
3	18
4	24
5	30
6	36
7	42
8	48
9	54

Some multiples of 4 are 4, 8, 12, 16, 20, 24, 28, 32, 36.
Some multiples of 6 are 6, 12, 18, 24, 30, 36, 42, 48, 54.
The numbers 12, 24 and 36 are multiples of 4 and multiples of 6.
They are called *common multiples* of 4 and 6.

Is the statement true or false? Write *T* or *F*.

1. 36 is a multiple of 6. ____
2. 8 is a multiple of 4. ____
3. 4 is a multiple of 4. ____
4. 2 is a multiple of 4. ____
5. 2 is a multiple of 6. ____
6. 3 is a multiple of 6. ____
7. 6 is a multiple of 6. ____
8. 42 is a multiple of 6. ____
9. 18 is a multiple of 3. ____
10. 3 is a multiple of 9. ____
11. 24 is a common multiple of 6 and 8. ____
12. 12 is a common multiple of 4 and 8. ____

Write the numbers.

13. the first five multiples of 3 _____
14. the first five multiples of 5 _____
15. a common multiple of 3 and 5 _____

Is the number even or odd? Write *E* or *O*.

16. 15 ____ 17. 10 ____ 18. 17 ____ 19. 21 ____ 20. 30 ____

21. 76 ____ 22. 87 ____ 23. 41 ____ 24. 52 ____ 25. 34 ____

United States senators are elected for 6 years. A senator was elected for his first term in 1982. Suppose he wins the next 6 elections. Write the year of this election.

26. 3rd ____ 27. 6th ____ 28. 4th ____

Stacey is taking guitar lessons. She learned 4 new songs each month during September, October, and November. During December, Stacey practiced less often. She learned only 2 new songs. How many new songs did Stacey learn in all?

This problem takes 2 steps to solve.

1. Multiply to find the total number of new songs that Stacey learned during September, October, and November. $\begin{array}{r} 3 \\ \times\ 4 \\ \hline 12 \end{array}$	**2.** Add the 2 new songs that Stacey learned during December. $\begin{array}{r} 12 \\ +\ 2 \\ \hline 14 \end{array}$ Answer: 14 new songs

Solve. Write the operations you used.

1. Gary is saving money to buy a guitar that costs $168. He has already saved $76. His parents are giving him $50 for the guitar. How much more money must Gary save? _____

2. Carolyn practices the piano 6 days a week. She practices 2 hours each day. Her piano teacher would like her to practice 15 hours each week. How many extra hours should she practice? _____

3. Scott spent 15 minutes of his violin lesson working on a new song. Then he practiced 6 old songs. He spent 5 minutes working on each one. How long was Scott's lesson? _____

_____

Use the chart to solve.

4. Mrs. Buckley gives music lessons. She charges $8 for each lesson. How much does she earn in a week? _____

Number of Students Each Week	
Piano	4
Guitar	3
Violin	2

Practice

5-1

There are 20 children in Armando's class. His teacher wants 4 desks in each row.

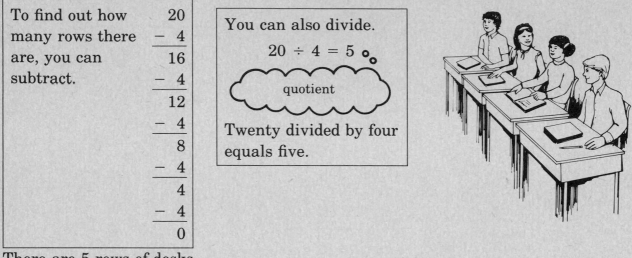

To find out how many rows there are, you can subtract.

$$\begin{array}{r} 20 \\ -\ 4 \\ \hline 16 \\ -\ 4 \\ \hline 12 \\ -\ 4 \\ \hline 8 \\ -\ 4 \\ \hline 4 \\ -\ 4 \\ \hline 0 \end{array}$$

You can also divide.

$20 \div 4 = 5$ quotient

Twenty divided by four equals five.

There are 5 rows of desks.

Divide.

1. $18 \div 2 =$ ____

2. $15 \div 3 =$ ____

3. $6 \div 3 =$ ____

4. $16 \div 4 =$ ____

5. $24 \div 4 =$ ____

6. $6 \div 2 =$ ____

7. $28 \div 4 =$ ____

8. $27 \div 3 =$ ____

9. $2\overline{)10}$

10. $3\overline{)9}$

11. $4\overline{)8}$

12. $2\overline{)14}$

13. $3\overline{)24}$

14. $2\overline{)2}$

15. $4\overline{)12}$

16. $3\overline{)12}$

How many

17. twos in 12? ____

18. threes in 21? ____

19. fours in 36? ____

20. twos in 8? ____

21. threes in 18? ____

22. fours in 32? ____

Solve.

23. Armando's class is divided into groups of 5 to study their spelling words. There are 20 students in the class. How many groups of 5 are there? _____

24. Armando's class is doing an experiment using a meter stick. His teacher wants 3 children to work together. If 2 children are absent, how many meter sticks are needed? _____

Practice

Student Book pp. 134–135

5-2

Cathy has 18 pictures to put in her photo album. She puts 3 pictures on each page.

To find out how many pages she uses, you divide.

$18 \div 3 = 6$ $\qquad 3)\overline{18}^{\;6}$

Cathy uses 6 pages.

Divide.

1. $24 \div 4 =$ _____
2. $18 \div 2 =$ _____
3. $6 \div 3 =$ _____
4. $20 \div 4 =$ _____

5. $2 \div 2 =$ _____
6. $15 \div 3 =$ _____
7. $21 \div 3 =$ _____
8. $14 \div 2 =$ _____

9. $9 \div 3 =$ _____
10. $36 \div 4 =$ _____
11. $28 \div 4 =$ _____
12. $18 \div 3 =$ _____

13. $6 \div 2 =$ _____
14. $3 \div 3 =$ _____
15. $8 \div 4 =$ _____
16. $12 \div 2 =$ _____

17. $16 \div 4 =$ _____
18. $8 \div 2 =$ _____
19. $4 \div 2 =$ _____
20. $24 \div 3 =$ _____

21. $3)\overline{12}$
22. $2)\overline{10}$
23. $4)\overline{16}$
24. $7)\overline{35}$

25. $4)\overline{4}$
26. $4)\overline{32}$
27. $2)\overline{14}$
28. $4)\overline{20}$

29. $2)\overline{12}$
30. $3)\overline{9}$
31. $2)\overline{16}$
32. $3)\overline{27}$

Use the graph to solve.

33. Cathy wants to put her pictures of the mountains and of the zoo in her photo album. She wants to use 3 pages and put the same number on each page. How many will she put on each page? _____

34. Cathy has just one page left in her photo album. Only 10 pictures will fit on a page. Does she have enough space to put all of her ocean pictures in her album?

_____

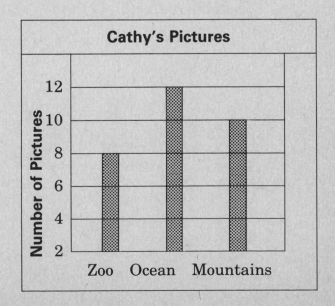

Cathy's Pictures

Name _____

Practice

Student Book pp. 136–137

5-3

Greg earned $25 mowing lawns. He gets $5 for each job. To find out how many lawns he mowed, use division.

$$25 \div 5 = 5 \quad \text{or} \quad 5\overline{)25}^{\,5}$$

Greg mowed 5 lawns.

Think: The answer makes sense because $5 + 5 + 5 + 5 + 5 = 25$

Divide.

1. $20 \div 5 =$ ____ **2.** $24 \div 4 =$ ____ **3.** $18 \div 2 =$ ____ **4.** $12 \div 4 =$ ____

5. $4 \div 4 =$ ____ **6.** $21 \div 3 =$ ____ **7.** $15 \div 5 =$ ____ **8.** $9 \div 3 =$ ____

9. $6 \div 2 =$ ____ **10.** $35 \div 5 =$ ____ **11.** $24 \div 3 =$ ____ **12.** $16 \div 4 =$ ____

13. $36 \div 4 =$ ____ **14.** $18 \div 3 =$ ____ **15.** $16 \div 2 =$ ____ **16.** $10 \div 5 =$ ____

17. $20 \div 4 =$ ____ **18.** $8 \div 4 =$ ____ **19.** $32 \div 4 =$ ____ **20.** $6 \div 3 =$ ____

21. $3\overline{)12}$ **22.** $5\overline{)25}$ **23.** $4\overline{)28}$ **24.** $3\overline{)27}$ **25.** $5\overline{)45}$

26. $5\overline{)5}$ **27.** $5\overline{)30}$ **28.** $3\overline{)15}$ **29.** $3\overline{)3}$ **30.** $5\overline{)40}$

The missing addends in the problems are all the same. Divide to find the missing numbers.

31. ☐ + ☐ + ☐ + ☐ = 8 **32.** ☐ + ☐ + ☐ + ☐ + ☐ = 40

Solve.

33. Greg earned $35 for trimming bushes. He worked for 5 different people. How much did he charge each person? _____

34. Greg usually spends 1 hour and 45 minutes to mow a lawn. There are 3 hours of daylight left after school. Can he mow 2 lawns after school before it gets dark? _____

Practice

Student Book pp. 138–139

5-4

Multiplication and division have fact families. This is the fact family for 4, 3, and 12.

$4 \times 3 = 12 \qquad 12 \div 3 = 4$
$3 \times 4 = 12 \qquad 12 \div 4 = 3$

You can check a division fact by multiplying.

Is this correct?   Check.

$$\begin{array}{r} 8 \\ 5\overline{)40} \end{array} \qquad \begin{array}{r} 8 \\ \times 5 \\ \hline 40 \end{array} \checkmark \quad \text{It checks.}$$

Remember:

When you divide 0 by a number, the quotient is 0. $8\overline{)0}$ (quotient 0)

When you divide any number by 1, the quotient is that number. $1\overline{)8}$ (quotient 8)

When you divide a number by itself, the quotient is 1. $8\overline{)8}$ (quotient 1)

You cannot divide a number by 0.

Divide. Check by multiplying.

1. $4\overline{)36}$ 2. $5\overline{)30}$ 3. $5\overline{)5}$ 4. $2\overline{)0}$ 5. $3\overline{)27}$ 6. $1\overline{)4}$

7. $3\overline{)21}$ 8. $4\overline{)4}$ 9. $2\overline{)14}$ 10. $4\overline{)20}$ 11. $2\overline{)4}$ 12. $5\overline{)25}$

13. $5\overline{)0}$ 14. $4\overline{)32}$ 15. $3\overline{)3}$ 16. $5\overline{)45}$ 17. $3\overline{)9}$ 18. $2\overline{)18}$

19. $4\overline{)16}$ 20. $1\overline{)3}$ 21. $4\overline{)28}$ 22. $3\overline{)18}$ 23. $2\overline{)2}$ 24. $2\overline{)12}$

Write the multiplication and division fact family for these numbers.

25. 2, 4, 8 _____

26. 3, 5, 15 _____

Write a number sentence. Solve.

27. There are 4 children going to the movies. Tickets cost $2 each. How much will it cost them to go to the movies? _____

28. Ms. Chin won 35 free passes to the movies. How many times can she and 4 friends go to the movies free? _____

Name _____

Practice

Student Book pp. 140–141

5-5

SHELL COLLECTION

Choose the correct plan.
Write *a, b, c,* or *d.* Then solve.

1. Peter collects shells. He displays them in special cases. In one case, there are 5 rows with 8 shells on each row. How many shells are there in the case?

   _____

   a. $5 + 8$ **b.** 5×8 **c.** $8 - 5$ **d.** $5\overline{)8}$

2. Tina collects rocks and shells. She has 23 more rocks than shells. If Tina has 32 shells, how many rocks does she have? _____

   a. $23 + 32$ **b.** 23×32 **c.** $32 - 23$ **d.** $23\overline{)32}$

3. Sandy collects toy cars. She has 25 cars in her collection. Her brother has 6 fewer cars. How many cars does her brother have? _____

   a. $25 + 6$ **b.** 25×6 **c.** $25 - 6$ **d.** $6\overline{)25}$

4. Greg, Gary, and Tom all collect shells. Together, they have 27 shells. They each have the same number of shells in their collections. How many shells do they each have? _____

   a. $27 + 3$ **b.** 27×3 **c.** $27 - 3$ **d.** $3\overline{)27}$

Solve.

5. A hobby store sells display cases. One case holds 21 dolls on 3 shelves. How many dolls will fit on 1 shelf?   _____

6. Emily puts each of the rocks she collects in a plastic case. She bought a package of small cases for $5.98 and a package of medium-size cases for $6.49. How much did she spend on plastic cases?   _____

Name _____

When you know the multiplication facts, you know division facts, too.

Think: How many sevens in 35?

$7\overline{)35}$
$\square \times 7 = 35$
$5 \times 7 = 35$
so, $7\overline{)35}^{\,5}$

XXXXXXX
XXXXXXX
XXXXXXX
XXXXXXX
XXXXXXX

5 sevens

How many sevens in 35?

Divide. Think of multiplication.

1. $21 \div 7 =$ _____ **2.** $6 \div 6 =$ _____ **3.** $30 \div 6 =$ _____ **4.** $49 \div 7 =$ _____

5. $18 \div 6 =$ _____ **6.** $28 \div 7 =$ _____ **7.** $7 \div 7 =$ _____ **8.** $24 \div 6 =$ _____

9. $0 \div 6 =$ _____ **10.** $24 \div 4 =$ _____ **11.** $30 \div 5 =$ _____ **12.** $18 \div 3 =$ _____

13. $2\overline{)14}$ **14.** $6\overline{)36}$ **15.** $4\overline{)16}$ **16.** $6\overline{)42}$ **17.** $5\overline{)20}$ **18.** $5\overline{)15}$

19. $6\overline{)12}$ **20.** $5\overline{)35}$ **21.** $7\overline{)0}$ **22.** $3\overline{)27}$ **23.** $4\overline{)32}$ **24.** $3\overline{)21}$

25. $4\overline{)28}$ **26.** $7\overline{)42}$ **27.** $3\overline{)24}$ **28.** $2\overline{)18}$ **29.** $6\overline{)54}$ **30.** $2\overline{)12}$

31. $4\overline{)36}$ **32.** $5\overline{)45}$ **33.** $7\overline{)63}$ **34.** $6\overline{)48}$ **35.** $7\overline{)56}$ **36.** $7\overline{)14}$

Think of a related multiplication or division fact to solve. Write only the missing number.

37. _____ $\div 6 = 7$ **38.** _____ $\times 7 = 35$ **39.** _____ $\div 7 = 7$ **40.** _____ $\times 6 = 36$

41. _____ $\times 4 = 24$ **42.** _____ $\div 3 = 7$ **43.** _____ $\times 2 = 4$ **44.** _____ $\div 5 = 3$

Is there enough information to solve the problem? Write *yes* or *no*. If your answer is yes, then solve.

45. Mr. Hancock is making a bookcase. He has a 12-ft piece of lumber for shelves. Does he have enough lumber for the shelves? _____

46. Sara works 10 hours. She earns $2.50 per hour. How much does she earn? _____

Practice

Mr. Kane owns a pet shop. He has 56 goldfish. He wants to put 8 goldfish in each tank. How many tanks will he need? You can use multiplication to help you divide.

$7 \times 8 = 56$ $8\overline{)56}$ → 7

He needs 7 tanks.

Divide.

1. $18 \div 9 =$ ___   **2.** $45 \div 9 =$ ___   **3.** $32 \div 8 =$ ___   **4.** $24 \div 8 =$ ___

5. $18 \div 3 =$ ___   **6.** $8 \div 8 =$ ___   **7.** $15 \div 5 =$ ___   **8.** $9 \div 9 =$ ___

9. $9\overline{)27}$ **10.** $5\overline{)40}$ **11.** $9\overline{)54}$ **12.** $6\overline{)48}$ **13.** $7\overline{)28}$ **14.** $9\overline{)81}$

15. $9\overline{)36}$ **16.** $8\overline{)64}$ **17.** $8\overline{)16}$ **18.** $3\overline{)27}$ **19.** $7\overline{)63}$ **20.** $6\overline{)36}$

21. $9\overline{)0}$ **22.** $8\overline{)40}$ **23.** $9\overline{)63}$ **24.** $7\overline{)56}$ **25.** $8\overline{)72}$ **26.** $6\overline{)42}$

Divide to find the first quotient. Use estimation to decide if the second quotient is *greater than* or *less than* the first.

27. $8\overline{)48}$ $6\overline{)48}$ _____   **28.** $2\overline{)16}$ $4\overline{)16}$ _____

29. $3\overline{)24}$ $4\overline{)24}$ _____   **30.** $9\overline{)72}$ $8\overline{)72}$ _____

Solve.

31. Crystal bought an angelfish and 5 goldfish. How much did she spend? _____

32. Mr. Kane received $40 from Dennis for some fantails. How many fantails did Dennis buy?

_____

Angelfish	$8 each
Fantails	$5 each
Goldfish	5 for $1

Name _____

Divide.

1. 15 ÷ 5 = _____   **2.** 9 ÷ 1 = _____   **3.** 24 ÷ 3 = _____   **4.** 0 ÷ 8 = _____

5. 18 ÷ 2 = _____   **6.** 36 ÷ 9 = _____   **7.** 27 ÷ 3 = _____   **8.** 25 ÷ 5 = _____

9. 30 ÷ 6 = _____   **10.** 28 ÷ 7 = _____   **11.** 28 ÷ 4 = _____   **12.** 48 ÷ 8 = _____

13. 2)‾12   **14.** 9)‾54   **15.** 4)‾24   **16.** 8)‾8   **17.** 6)‾18   **18.** 7)‾0

19. 3)‾15   **20.** 7)‾35   **21.** 4)‾4   **22.** 5)‾20   **23.** 9)‾45   **24.** 8)‾32

25. 7)‾21   **26.** 8)‾16   **27.** 6)‾42   **28.** 3)‾21   **29.** 9)‾63   **30.** 5)‾5

31. 6)‾12   **32.** 7)‾42   **33.** 1)‾4   **34.** 8)‾64   **35.** 5)‾10   **36.** 9)‾18

37. 2)‾14   **38.** 3)‾9   **39.** 6)‾6   **40.** 8)‾24   **41.** 7)‾14   **42.** 8)‾56

43. 5)‾40   **44.** 4)‾36   **45.** 7)‾63   **46.** 3)‾12   **47.** 1)‾7   **48.** 9)‾27

49. 6)‾48   **50.** 2)‾2   **51.** 4)‾32   **52.** 6)‾24   **53.** 4)‾16   **54.** 7)‾49

55. 4)‾20   **56.** 3)‾0   **57.** 4)‾8   **58.** 7)‾7   **59.** 6)‾36   **60.** 5)‾30

Solve.

61. Claire earned $48 working at the book store. If she worked 6 hours, how much does she earn an hour? _____

62. Claire unpacked 36 books and placed them on 4 shelves. She placed the same number of books on each shelf. How many books are on each shelf? _____

Lisa is putting 25 photos from her summer vacation into a photo album. She is putting 4 photos on each page. How many pages will she fill completely? How many will go on the page that is not completely filled?

To divide 25 by 4, you subtract as many fours as possible.

$$\begin{array}{r} 6 \\ 4\overline{)25} \\ -24 \\ \hline 1 \end{array} \leftarrow \text{remainder}$$

Subtract
6 groups of 4.
$6 \times 4 = 24$

XXXX
XXXX
XXXX
XXXX
XXXX
XXXX
XXXX
X ⟵ 1 left over

Write the quotient with the remainder.

$$\begin{array}{r} 6\,R1 \\ 4\overline{)25} \\ -24 \\ \hline 1 \end{array}$$

The remainder should always be less than the number we divide by.

Divide.

1. $3\overline{)19}$　　**2.** $5\overline{)27}$　　**3.** $6\overline{)20}$　　**4.** $2\overline{)9}$　　**5.** $8\overline{)43}$　　**6.** $2\overline{)15}$

7. $5\overline{)47}$　　**8.** $9\overline{)56}$　　**9.** $6\overline{)28}$　　**10.** $7\overline{)50}$　　**11.** $3\overline{)26}$　　**12.** $8\overline{)18}$

13. $4\overline{)33}$　　**14.** $4\overline{)19}$　　**15.** $5\overline{)34}$　　**16.** $9\overline{)51}$　　**17.** $8\overline{)54}$　　**18.** $6\overline{)40}$

While studying a unit on Early American crafts, some fourth grade students decided to make a patchwork quilt. Solve these problems about their project.

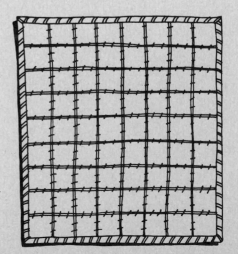

19. The quilt is made of 9 rows of squares. There are 8 squares in each row. How many squares are there in all? _____

20. After several weeks of work, the students completed 50 squares. There are 8 squares in a row. How many rows are completed? _____

How many squares are left over?

_____

Practice
Student Book pp. 150–151

5-10

Find the common factors of each pair of
numbers. Then use a ruler to draw
squares to connect the pairs of numbers
that have the same common factors.

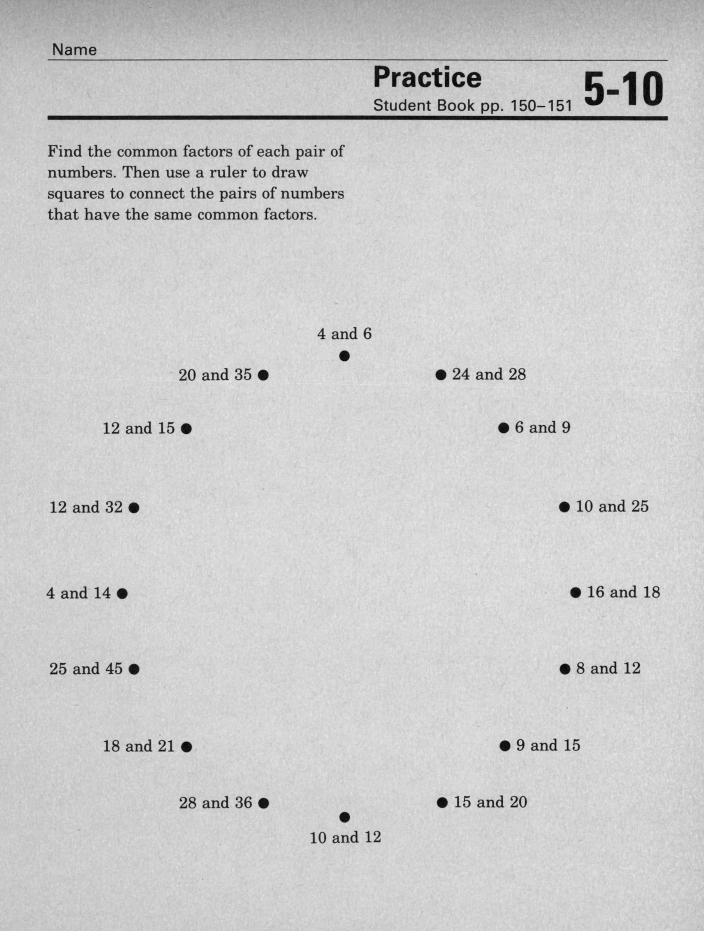

4 and 6

20 and 35

24 and 28

12 and 15

6 and 9

12 and 32

10 and 25

4 and 14

16 and 18

25 and 45

8 and 12

18 and 21

9 and 15

28 and 36

15 and 20

10 and 12

Practice
Student Book pp. 152–153

The Youngtown Youth Club had a car wash. They charged $2.50 to wash each car. They washed 23 cars in the morning and 17 cars in the afternoon. How many cars did they wash in all?

```
   23  cars in the morning
 + 17  cars in the afternoon
   40
```

They washed 40 cars in all.

You did not need to know how much they charged to wash a car to solve the problem.

Underline the fact you do *not* need to answer the question. Solve.

1. There are 20 members in the club. Only 16 of them worked at the car wash. Half the workers brought sponges. How many sponges did they have? _____

2. John worked 40 minutes in the morning and 30 minutes in the afternoon. Joan worked an hour in the morning. How long did John work altogether? _____

3. The club charged $2.50 to wash a car. They charged another $.50 to dry it. Mr. Robertson had a $5 bill. How much change did he receive if he just had his car washed? _____

4. A group of 4 members worked together to wash each car. It takes them 8 minutes to wash one car. If they work at the same rate, how long will it take to wash 6 cars? _____

5. To buy the supplies for the car wash, $30 was donated to the club. One team of 4 earned $36 washing cars during the first hour of the car wash. How much did each member of the team earn during the first hour? _____

6. The Youth Club had 8 buckets altogether. They borrowed 5 buckets and bought 3. If there are 16 members working at the car wash, how many members share each bucket? _____

Practice

Student Book pp. 162–163

6-1

Sometimes you can use patterns to multiply large numbers.

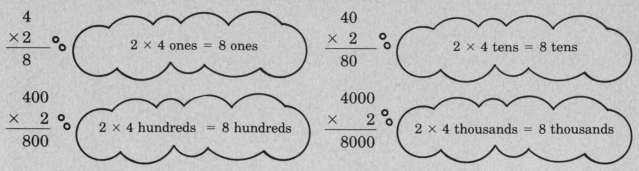

$\begin{array}{r} 4 \\ \times 2 \\ \hline 8 \end{array}$ 2 × 4 ones = 8 ones

$\begin{array}{r} 40 \\ \times 2 \\ \hline 80 \end{array}$ 2 × 4 tens = 8 tens

$\begin{array}{r} 400 \\ \times 2 \\ \hline 800 \end{array}$ 2 × 4 hundreds = 8 hundreds

$\begin{array}{r} 4000 \\ \times 2 \\ \hline 8000 \end{array}$ 2 × 4 thousands = 8 thousands

You can multiply numbers like these mentally. The number of zeros in the factors tells you how many zeros are in the product.

Multiply.

1. $\begin{array}{r} 40 \\ \times 3 \\ \hline \end{array}$	**2.** $\begin{array}{r} 500 \\ \times 4 \\ \hline \end{array}$	**3.** $\begin{array}{r} 4000 \\ \times 4 \\ \hline \end{array}$	**4.** $\begin{array}{r} 3000 \\ \times 9 \\ \hline \end{array}$	**5.** $\begin{array}{r} 60 \\ \times 6 \\ \hline \end{array}$	**6.** $\begin{array}{r} 800 \\ \times 3 \\ \hline \end{array}$
7. $\begin{array}{r} 5000 \\ \times 3 \\ \hline \end{array}$	**8.** $\begin{array}{r} 6000 \\ \times 7 \\ \hline \end{array}$	**9.** $\begin{array}{r} 70 \\ \times 4 \\ \hline \end{array}$	**10.** $\begin{array}{r} 300 \\ \times 6 \\ \hline \end{array}$	**11.** $\begin{array}{r} 9000 \\ \times 5 \\ \hline \end{array}$	**12.** $\begin{array}{r} 4000 \\ \times 8 \\ \hline \end{array}$
13. $\begin{array}{r} 20 \\ \times 8 \\ \hline \end{array}$	**14.** $\begin{array}{r} 700 \\ \times 5 \\ \hline \end{array}$	**15.** $\begin{array}{r} 7000 \\ \times 2 \\ \hline \end{array}$	**16.** $\begin{array}{r} 9000 \\ \times 8 \\ \hline \end{array}$	**17.** $\begin{array}{r} 80 \\ \times 6 \\ \hline \end{array}$	**18.** $\begin{array}{r} 200 \\ \times 8 \\ \hline \end{array}$
19. $\begin{array}{r} 2000 \\ \times 5 \\ \hline \end{array}$	**20.** $\begin{array}{r} 2000 \\ \times 4 \\ \hline \end{array}$	**21.** $\begin{array}{r} 90 \\ \times 3 \\ \hline \end{array}$	**22.** $\begin{array}{r} 600 \\ \times 7 \\ \hline \end{array}$	**23.** $\begin{array}{r} 8000 \\ \times 8 \\ \hline \end{array}$	**24.** $\begin{array}{r} 4000 \\ \times 9 \\ \hline \end{array}$

Complete the table.

25.

Tons	1	2	3	4	5	6	7	8	9
Pounds	2000								

Solve.

26. There are 200 pieces in a building set. How many pieces are in 8 sets? _____

27. There are 40 round pieces in 1 building set. It takes 5 round pieces to make a robot. How many robots can be made from 1 building set? _____

Practice

Student Book pp. 164–165

The Sports Club ordered new team uniforms. They ordered 12 uniforms for each team. If there are 8 teams, about how many uniforms did they order?

When a question asks "about how many", you don't need an exact answer. Estimate by rounding the factor greater than 10 to its greatest place value.

$$
\begin{array}{ccc}
 & \text{Round 12} & \text{Multiply} \\
12 \longrightarrow & 10 & 10 \\
\underline{\times\ 8} & \underline{\times\ 8} & \underline{\times\ 8} \\
 & & 80
\end{array}
$$

They ordered about 80 uniforms.

Round the factor greater than 10 to its greatest place value. Estimate the product.

1. 38 $\times\ 4$	**2.** 37 $\times\ 5$	**3.** 62 $\times\ 9$	**4.** 59 $\times\ 6$	**5.** 45 $\times\ 3$
6. 435 $\times\ 2$	**7.** 893 $\times\ 3$	**8.** 450 $\times\ 4$	**9.** 293 $\times\ 4$	**10.** 751 $\times\ 3$
11. 4367 $\times\ 8$	**12.** 1643 $\times\ 7$	**13.** 3109 $\times\ 6$	**14.** 8876 $\times\ 5$	**15.** 7389 $\times\ 7$
16. 364 $\times\ 9$	**17.** 2321 $\times\ 2$	**18.** 36 $\times\ 8$	**19.** 847 $\times\ 6$	**20.** 6510 $\times\ 5$

21. $3 \times 46 =$ _____

22. $8 \times 651 =$ _____

23. $2 \times 5561 =$ _____

24. $7 \times 326 =$ _____

25. $9 \times 83 =$ _____

26. $4 \times 9076 =$ _____

Estimate to solve.

27. The Sports Club ordered 18 boxes of basketballs. Each box contains 4 balls. About how many balls did they order?

_____

28. There were 78 members of the Sports Club. This fall 33 new members joined. About how many members are there now?

_____

Practice

Student Book pp. 166–167

The pet store has 2 tanks of goldfish.
There are 43 goldfish in each tank.
How many goldfish are there in all?
You multiply 2 × 43 to find the
number of goldfish.

Multiply 3 ones
by 2.

t	o
4	3
×	2
	6

Multiply 4 tens
by 2.

t	o
4	3
×	2
8	6

There are 86 goldfish.

Multiply.

1.	13 × 3	2.	24 × 2	3.	40 × 2	4.	13 × 2	5.	14 × 2	6.	10 × 9

7.	21 × 2	8.	41 × 2	9.	11 × 4	10.	10 × 3	11.	12 × 2	12.	33 × 3

13. 4 × 12 = _____   **14.** 4 × 21 = _____   **15.** 2 × 23 = _____

16. 3 × 21 = _____   **17.** 3 × 22 = _____   **18.** 4 × 20 = _____

Solve.

19. Is the product of 4 and 22 greater than or less than the
product of 3 and 23? _____

20. It takes Tom 11 minutes to clean a fish tank. There are 2
tanks of goldfish and 3 tanks of guppies. How much time
does Tom spend cleaning the fish tanks?

_____

Practice

Student Book pp. 168–169

Let's multiply 37 by 2.
Multiply the 7 ones by 2.
Rename 14 as 1 ten 4 ones.

Multiply the 3 tens by 2.
Add the 1 ten.

t	o
1	
3	7
×	2
	4

$7 \times 2 = 14$
14 is 1 ten 4 ones.

t	o
1	
3	7
×	2
7	4

3 tens × 2 = 6 tens
6 tens + 1 = 7 tens

Multiply.

1. 14 ×3	**2.** 15 ×2	**3.** 14 ×5	**4.** 12 ×6	**5.** 16 ×5	**6.** 18 ×3
7. 23 ×4	**8.** 32 ×2	**9.** 24 ×3	**10.** 12 ×5	**11.** 17 ×4	**12.** 13 ×6
13. 15 ×4	**14.** 35 ×2	**15.** 19 ×4	**16.** 39 ×2	**17.** 22 ×3	**18.** 14 ×4

Use mental math to solve. Write only the answer.

19. $4 \times 16 =$ ___   **20.** $3 \times 23 =$ ___   **21.** $6 \times 14 =$ ___   **22.** $2 \times 38 =$ ___

23. $3 \times 28 =$ ___   **24.** $7 \times 13 =$ ___   **25.** $5 \times 13 =$ ___   **26.** $2 \times 29 =$ ___

Use mental math or paper and pencil to solve the problem.
Write *m* or *p* beside your answer to tell the method you chose.

27. There are 3 classes going on a trip to the seashore. Each class has 26 children. How many children are going on the trip? _____

28. At the shore, Eric collected 27 seashells and put them in 3 pails. How many shells does he have in each pail? _____

Practice

Student Book pp. 170–171

Eduardo works in the flower shop. He wants to put 5 roses in each vase. How many roses will he need to fill 27 vases?

To find out, multiply 27 by 5.

Multiply the 7 ones by 5.
Rename 35 as 3 tens 5 ones.

Multiply the 2 tens by 5.
Add the 3 tens.

$$\begin{array}{r} 3 \\ 27 \\ \times\ 5 \\ \hline 5 \end{array}$$

$5 \times 7 = 35$

$$\begin{array}{r} 3 \\ 27 \\ \times\ 5 \\ \hline 135 \end{array}$$

5×2 tens $= 10$ tens
10 tens $+ 3$ tens $= 13$ tens

Multiply.

1. $\begin{array}{r}84\\\times 3\end{array}$	2. $\begin{array}{r}45\\\times 6\end{array}$	3. $\begin{array}{r}78\\\times 4\end{array}$	4. $\begin{array}{r}64\\\times 5\end{array}$	5. $\begin{array}{r}65\\\times 3\end{array}$	6. $\begin{array}{r}55\\\times 5\end{array}$
7. $\begin{array}{r}73\\\times 8\end{array}$	8. $\begin{array}{r}51\\\times 6\end{array}$	9. $\begin{array}{r}36\\\times 7\end{array}$	10. $\begin{array}{r}60\\\times 7\end{array}$	11. $\begin{array}{r}23\\\times 3\end{array}$	12. $\begin{array}{r}95\\\times 3\end{array}$

13. $9 \times 24 =$ _____   14. $2 \times 36 =$ _____   15. $6 \times 57 =$ _____

Estimate the product. Then tell whether the actual product will be greater than or less than the estimate.

16. $4 \times 52 =$ _____   17. $6 \times 89 =$ _____

18. $2 \times 66 =$ _____   19. $9 \times 48 =$ _____

20. $7 \times 55 =$ _____   21. $6 \times 31 =$ _____

Some problems have too much or too little information. Solve the problem or tell what you need to know.

22. The florist shop orders flowers by the box. Each box contains 24 flowers. On Monday, 6 boxes of carnations and 5 boxes of roses were delivered to the shop. How many boxes were delivered in all? _____

23. Holiday flower arrangements contain 26 flowers. Orders for these arrangements are taken up to 2 days before the holiday. How many flowers will the florist need to make the arrangements that have been ordered? _____

Practice

Student Book pp. 172–173

6-6

The pictograph at the right shows the results of a poll at Vera's school. Each picture stands for 25 students who like a given sport the most. To find how many students like basketball the most multiply 5 × 25.

$$\begin{array}{r} 2 \\ 25 \\ \times\ 5 \\ \hline 125 \end{array}$$

Favorite Sports

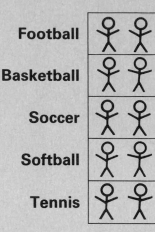

| Football |
| Basketball |
| Soccer |
| Softball |
| Tennis |

Each 👤 means 25 students.

There are 125 students who like basketball the best.

Use the pictograph to solve.

1. What sport do most of the students like best? _____

2. What sport do the least number of students like best? _____

3. How many students like softball best? _____

4. How many students like football best? _____

5. How many students like soccer best? _____

6. How many students like tennis best? _____

7. How many more students prefer soccer to tennis? _____

8. How many students in all like the two most favorite sports? _____

9. How many students in all like the two least favorite sports? _____

10. How many students took part in the poll? _____

To multiply 168 by 4, you need to rename twice. Remember that 10 tens equal 1 hundred.

Multiply the 8 ones by 4. Rename 32 ones as 3 tens 2 ones.	Multiply the 6 tens by 4 and add the 3 tens. Rename 27 tens as 2 hundreds 7 tens.	Multiply the 1 hundred by 4 and add the 2 hundreds.
$$\begin{array}{r} 3 \\ 168 \\ \times\ 4 \\ \hline 2 \end{array}$$	$$\begin{array}{r} 23 \\ 168 \\ \times\ 4 \\ \hline 72 \end{array}$$	$$\begin{array}{r} 23 \\ 168 \\ \times\ 4 \\ \hline 672 \end{array}$$

Multiply.

1. $\begin{array}{r} 134 \\ \times\ 5 \end{array}$ **2.** $\begin{array}{r} 236 \\ \times\ 3 \end{array}$ **3.** $\begin{array}{r} 238 \\ \times\ 4 \end{array}$ **4.** $\begin{array}{r} 195 \\ \times\ 3 \end{array}$ **5.** $\begin{array}{r} 275 \\ \times\ 2 \end{array}$ **6.** $\begin{array}{r} 386 \\ \times\ 2 \end{array}$

7. $\begin{array}{r} 267 \\ \times\ 3 \end{array}$ **8.** $\begin{array}{r} 128 \\ \times\ 7 \end{array}$ **9.** $\begin{array}{r} 249 \\ \times\ 3 \end{array}$ **10.** $\begin{array}{r} 193 \\ \times\ 5 \end{array}$ **11.** $\begin{array}{r} 406 \\ \times\ 2 \end{array}$ **12.** $\begin{array}{r} 233 \\ \times\ 4 \end{array}$

13. $\begin{array}{r} 124 \\ \times\ 8 \end{array}$ **14.** $\begin{array}{r} 243 \\ \times\ 4 \end{array}$ **15.** $\begin{array}{r} 163 \\ \times\ 6 \end{array}$ **16.** $\begin{array}{r} 247 \\ \times\ 3 \end{array}$ **17.** $\begin{array}{r} 485 \\ \times\ 2 \end{array}$ **18.** $\begin{array}{r} 154 \\ \times\ 5 \end{array}$

19. $2 \times 306 = $ _____

20. $4 \times 237 = $ _____

21. $2 \times 458 = $ _____

22. $7 \times 133 = $ _____

Solve.

23. Mr. Trevino stacks soup cans on 3 shelves in his store. He puts 275 cans on each shelf. How many cans of soup are there in all?

_____

24. Mr. Trevino received an order of 92 boxes of oatmeal. He had 12 boxes of oatmeal on hand. How much oatmeal did he have then?

_____

Practice

Student Book pp. 176–177

The movie theater seats 584 people. On Saturday, the movie is shown 3 times. How many people can see the movie on Saturday?

To find out, multiply 584 by 3. Remember that 10 hundreds equal 1 thousand.

Multiply the 4 ones by 3. Rename 12 as 1 ten 2 ones.	Multiply the 8 tens by 3 and add the 1 ten. Rename 25 as 2 hundreds 5 tens.	Multiply the 5 hundreds by 3 and add the 2 hundreds.
$\begin{array}{r} 1 \\ 584 \\ \times\ \ 3 \\ \hline 2 \end{array}$	$\begin{array}{r} 2\,1 \\ 584 \\ \times\ \ 3 \\ \hline 52 \end{array}$	$\begin{array}{r} 2\,1 \\ 584 \\ \times\ \ 3 \\ \hline 1752 \end{array}$

On Saturday, 1752 people can see the movie.

Multiply.

1. $\begin{array}{r} 437 \\ \times\ \ 3 \\ \hline \end{array}$
2. $\begin{array}{r} 535 \\ \times\ \ 4 \\ \hline \end{array}$
3. $\begin{array}{r} 678 \\ \times\ \ 2 \\ \hline \end{array}$
4. $\begin{array}{r} 536 \\ \times\ \ 3 \\ \hline \end{array}$
5. $\begin{array}{r} 825 \\ \times\ \ 4 \\ \hline \end{array}$

6. $\begin{array}{r} 482 \\ \times\ \ 5 \\ \hline \end{array}$
7. $\begin{array}{r} 587 \\ \times\ \ 2 \\ \hline \end{array}$
8. $\begin{array}{r} 472 \\ \times\ \ 6 \\ \hline \end{array}$
9. $\begin{array}{r} 794 \\ \times\ \ 4 \\ \hline \end{array}$
10. $\begin{array}{r} 736 \\ \times\ \ 6 \\ \hline \end{array}$

11. $\begin{array}{r} 429 \\ \times\ \ 5 \\ \hline \end{array}$
12. $\begin{array}{r} 593 \\ \times\ \ 4 \\ \hline \end{array}$
13. $\begin{array}{r} 472 \\ \times\ \ 5 \\ \hline \end{array}$
14. $\begin{array}{r} 328 \\ \times\ \ 3 \\ \hline \end{array}$
15. $\begin{array}{r} 836 \\ \times\ \ 5 \\ \hline \end{array}$

Use the table to solve.

16. During the holidays the film at Movie II is shown 6 times a day. Can more than 1800 people see the film in one day?

Number of Seats	
Movie I	230
Movie II	315
Movie III	584

_____

17. A movie can be shown at both Movie I and Movie II or it can be shown at Movie III. Which arrangement will allow more people to see the movie?

_____

Practice

Student Book pp. 178–179

You need to rename 3 times when you multiply 4547 by 3.

Multiply the 7 ones by 3. Write the 1. Remember the 2 tens.	$\begin{array}{r} \overset{2}{4547} \\ \times\ \ \ 3 \\ \hline 1 \end{array}$	$3 \times 7 = 21$

Multiply the 4 tens by 3 and add the 2 tens. Write the 4. Remember the 1 hundred.	$\begin{array}{r} \overset{1\,2}{4547} \\ \times\ \ \ 3 \\ \hline 41 \end{array}$	3×4 tens $= 12$ tens 12 tens $+ 2$ tens $= 14$ tens

Multiply the 5 hundreds by 3 and add the 1 hundred. Write the 6. Remember the 1 thousand.	$\begin{array}{r} \overset{1\,1\,2}{4547} \\ \times\ \ \ 3 \\ \hline 641 \end{array}$	3×5 hundreds $= 15$ hundreds 15 hundreds $+ 1$ hundred $=$ 16 hundreds

Multiply the 4 thousands by 3 and add the 1 thousand. Write the 13.	$\begin{array}{r} \overset{1\,1\,2}{4547} \\ \times\ \ \ 3 \\ \hline 13{,}641 \end{array}$	3×4 thousands $= 12$ thousands 12 thousands $+ 1$ thousand $=$ 13 thousands

Multiply.

1.	$\begin{array}{r} 2635 \\ \times\ \ 2 \\ \hline \end{array}$	**2.**	$\begin{array}{r} 1852 \\ \times\ \ 3 \\ \hline \end{array}$	**3.**	$\begin{array}{r} 2839 \\ \times\ \ 3 \\ \hline \end{array}$	**4.**	$\begin{array}{r} 4594 \\ \times\ \ 2 \\ \hline \end{array}$	**5.**	$\begin{array}{r} 1257 \\ \times\ \ 4 \\ \hline \end{array}$

6.	$\begin{array}{r} 4245 \\ \times\ \ 7 \\ \hline \end{array}$	**7.**	$\begin{array}{r} 8657 \\ \times\ \ 4 \\ \hline \end{array}$	**8.**	$\begin{array}{r} 2357 \\ \times\ \ 5 \\ \hline \end{array}$	**9.**	$\begin{array}{r} 6425 \\ \times\ \ 4 \\ \hline \end{array}$	**10.**	$\begin{array}{r} 7194 \\ \times\ \ 2 \\ \hline \end{array}$

11.	$\begin{array}{r} 4951 \\ \times\ \ 4 \\ \hline \end{array}$	**12.**	$\begin{array}{r} 3772 \\ \times\ \ 6 \\ \hline \end{array}$	**13.**	$\begin{array}{r} 1725 \\ \times\ \ 7 \\ \hline \end{array}$	**14.**	$\begin{array}{r} 1624 \\ \times\ \ 8 \\ \hline \end{array}$	**15.**	$\begin{array}{r} 3714 \\ \times\ \ 3 \\ \hline \end{array}$

16. $1317 \times 9 =$ _____

17. $4132 \times 6 =$ _____

Solve.

18. The cows at the dairy farm produce 4375 liters of milk a day. How many liters of milk do they produce in 7 days? _____

Practice
Student Book pp. 180–181

To play this game choose a number from the circle and from the rectangle. Cross out the numbers. Find the product of the two numbers. Then, find the point value of the product. Write down the point value as your score. Now a second player does the same thing. If a player makes an error multiplying, the other player scores 1 bonus point. This is repeated until all the numbers have been crossed out. Add up the scores. The player with more points wins.

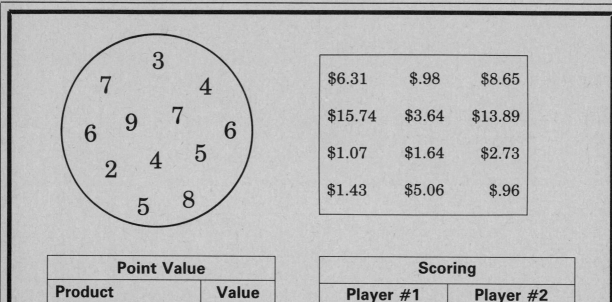

$6.31	$.98	$8.65
$15.74	$3.64	$13.89
$1.07	$1.64	$2.73
$1.43	$5.06	$.96

Point Value	
Product	**Value**
$ 1.00 - $ 3.00	1
$ 3.01 - $10.00	2
$10.01 - $20.00	3
$20.01 - $50.00	2
$50.01 and up	1

Scoring	
Player #1	**Player #2**

Practice

Student Book pp. 182–183

For a quick mental estimate when you work with money, you can round the amount to its greatest place value.

Mrs. Cohens bought 6 new chairs for $7.99 each. About how much did she spend?

Round to the nearest dollar.
Then multiply.

$$\$7.99 \longrightarrow \$8.00$$
$$\underline{\times\ 6} \qquad \underline{\times\ 6}$$
$$\$48.00$$

Mrs. Cohens spent about $48.00.

Match the problem and the estimate.

1. Micky bought 2 tickets to the movies. Each ticket cost $4.25. About how much did he spend? _____

2. Abigail bought a bracelet for $2.79. She gave the clerk $5.00. Estimate her change. _____

3. Mr. Hernandez spent $.98 for bread, $1.27 for milk, and $2.51 for butter. About how much did he spend in all? _____

A. $2.00

B. $5.00

C. $8.00

Estimate the answer.

4. Miss Johnson bought 5 books at $11.50 each. About how much did she spend? _____

5. Casey bought a blouse for $5.79 and a belt for $3.36. About how much money did she spend for both? _____

6. Mr. Robinson bought four items at the hardware store. The items cost $1.46, $.59, $7.95, and $1.87. Estimate the total cost of the items. _____

7. Barbara spent $16.38 for Mother's Day gifts. About how much of her $29.41 is left? _____

Practice

Student Book pp. 192–193

7-1

It takes two steps to divide 84 by 4.

4)84

Divide 8 tens by 4.

$$\begin{array}{r} 2 \\ 4\overline{)84} \\ -8 \\ \hline 0 \end{array}$$

Subtract 2 × 4.

Divide 4 ones by 4.

$$\begin{array}{r} 21 \\ 4\overline{)84} \\ -8\downarrow \\ \hline 4 \\ -4 \\ \hline 0 \end{array}$$

Subtract 1 × 4.

To check your answer
multiply the quotient by the divisor.

$$\begin{array}{r} 21 \\ \times\ 4 \\ \hline 84 \end{array}$$

Divide and check.

1. 3)66   **2.** 5)50   **3.** 4)44   **4.** 2)68   **5.** 3)93

6. 4)48   **7.** 3)63   **8.** 9)99   **9.** 5)55   **10.** 2)88

11. 8)80   **12.** 7)77   **13.** 2)46   **14.** 3)69   **15.** 4)48

16. 3)99   **17.** 2)28   **18.** 6)66   **19.** 8)88   **20.** 2)84

Solve.

21. A ship with 3 decks has 96 portholes. Each deck has the
same number of portholes. How many portholes are on
each deck? _____

22. A ship sailing to Bermuda has 32 passenger cabins on each
deck. It has 4 decks. How many passenger cabins does the
ship have in all? _____

Practice

Student Book pp. 194–195

When you divide 97 by 3, you have a remainder.

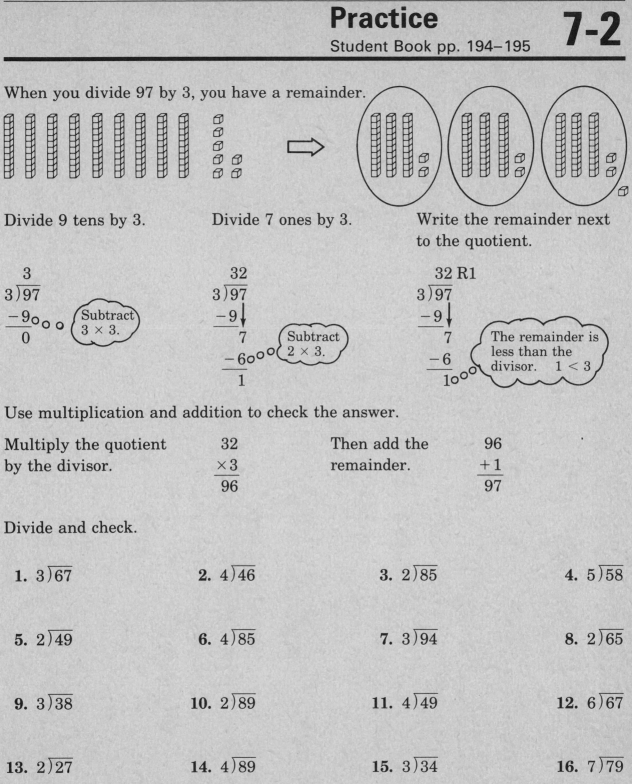

Divide 9 tens by 3.

Divide 7 ones by 3.

Write the remainder next to the quotient.

$$3\overline{)97}$$
3
−9 — Subtract 3 × 3.
0

$$3\overline{)97}$$
32
−9↓
7 — Subtract 2 × 3.
−6
1

$$3\overline{)97}$$
32 R1
−9↓
7
−6
1 — The remainder is less than the divisor. 1 < 3

Use multiplication and addition to check the answer.

Multiply the quotient by the divisor.

32
×3
96

Then add the remainder.

96
+1
97

Divide and check.

1. $3\overline{)67}$ 2. $4\overline{)46}$ 3. $2\overline{)85}$ 4. $5\overline{)58}$

5. $2\overline{)49}$ 6. $4\overline{)85}$ 7. $3\overline{)94}$ 8. $2\overline{)65}$

9. $3\overline{)38}$ 10. $2\overline{)89}$ 11. $4\overline{)49}$ 12. $6\overline{)67}$

13. $2\overline{)27}$ 14. $4\overline{)89}$ 15. $3\overline{)34}$ 16. $7\overline{)79}$

Solve.

17. There are 25 chairs to be divided evenly into 2 rows. How many chairs will be in each row? How many will be left over? _____

Name _____

This is how you divide 95 by 4.

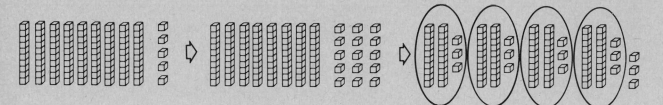

Divide 9 tens by 4.

Divide 15 ones by 4. Write the remainder with the quotient.

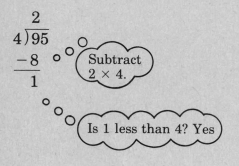

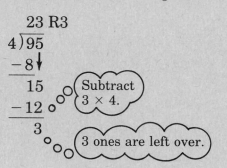

Divide.

1. $2\overline{)35}$ 2. $4\overline{)58}$ 3. $5\overline{)67}$ 4. $3\overline{)79}$ 5. $2\overline{)51}$

6. $7\overline{)99}$ 7. $4\overline{)96}$ 8. $5\overline{)96}$ 9. $8\overline{)95}$ 10. $2\overline{)38}$

11. $3\overline{)46}$ 12. $6\overline{)77}$ 13. $2\overline{)91}$ 14. $4\overline{)53}$ 15. $7\overline{)81}$

Estimate. Will the quotient be greater than 10?
Write *yes* or *no*.

16. $2\overline{)35}$ ____ 17. $5\overline{)62}$ ____ 18. $3\overline{)29}$ ____ 19. $6\overline{)52}$ ____ 20. $8\overline{)84}$ ____

Solve.

21. There are 36 children waiting to ride the zoo train. The train has 7 cars and each car holds 5 people. Will all the children get a seat on the next train? _____

Practice

Student Book pp. 198–199

7-4

This is how you divide 135 by 8.
There are not enough hundreds to divide by 8.
Think of 1 hundred 3 tens as 13 tens.

Divide the 13 tens by 8.

$$
\begin{array}{r}
1 \\
8\overline{)135} \\
-8 \\
\hline
5
\end{array}
$$

Divide the 55 ones by 8.
Write the remainder with the quotient.

$$
\begin{array}{r}
16\ \mathrm{R}7 \\
8\overline{)135} \\
-8\downarrow \\
\hline
55 \\
-48 \\
\hline
7
\end{array}
$$

Divide.

1. $8\overline{)421}$ **2.** $4\overline{)327}$ **3.** $5\overline{)234}$ **4.** $3\overline{)245}$ **5.** $2\overline{)157}$

6. $7\overline{)419}$ **7.** $9\overline{)874}$ **8.** $6\overline{)348}$ **9.** $4\overline{)155}$ **10.** $2\overline{)136}$

11. $9\overline{)356}$ **12.** $3\overline{)215}$ **13.** $8\overline{)462}$ **14.** $4\overline{)218}$ **15.** $5\overline{)435}$

16. $2\overline{)195}$ **17.** $8\overline{)273}$ **18.** $7\overline{)235}$ **19.** $6\overline{)391}$ **20.** $4\overline{)355}$

Use the information from the table to solve the problem.

21. The 4th grade is going on a field trip. Is it possible to put an equal number of students on 4 buses? _____

22. The 3rd and 4th grades eat lunch at the same time. How many chairs are needed in the cafeteria for this group? _____

Class	Students
3rd grade	178
4th grade	204
5th grade	188
6th grade	197

Practice

Student Book pp. 200–201

You must decide how to use the remainder in a division problem so that the quotient makes sense.
Here are two examples.

Judy is inviting 30 friends to a party. Invitations are sold in packages of 8. How many packages should Judy buy so that she can send all 30 friends an invitation?	Judy is serving sandwiches at the party. She has 75 slices of whole wheat bread. How many whole sandwiches can she make?

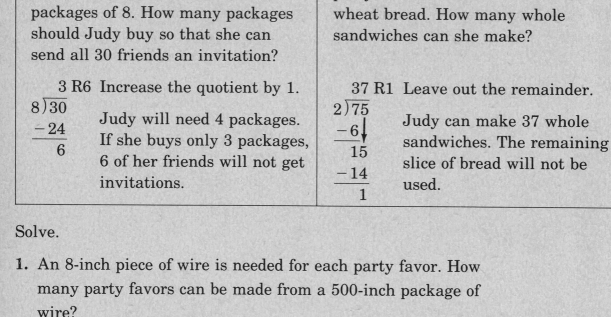

$$\begin{array}{r} 3\text{ R}6 \\ 8\overline{)30} \\ -24 \\ \hline 6 \end{array}$$

Increase the quotient by 1.

Judy will need 4 packages. If she buys only 3 packages, 6 of her friends will not get invitations.

$$\begin{array}{r} 37\text{ R}1 \\ 2\overline{)75} \\ -6\downarrow \\ \hline 15 \\ -14 \\ \hline 1 \end{array}$$

Leave out the remainder.

Judy can make 37 whole sandwiches. The remaining slice of bread will not be used.

Solve.

1. An 8-inch piece of wire is needed for each party favor. How many party favors can be made from a 500-inch package of wire? _____

2. Judy has 62 party favors. She wants to put the same number of favors at each of 4 tables. How many favors should she put at each table? _____

3. Judy can carry 6 glasses of milk from the kitchen at one time. How many trips from the kitchen must she make to give 27 people at the party a glass of milk? _____

4. Alan, Marc, and Lisa are bringing records to the party. How many records should each of them bring so that there will be at least 35 records at the party? _____

Practice

Student Book pp. 202–203

Divide 528 by 4.

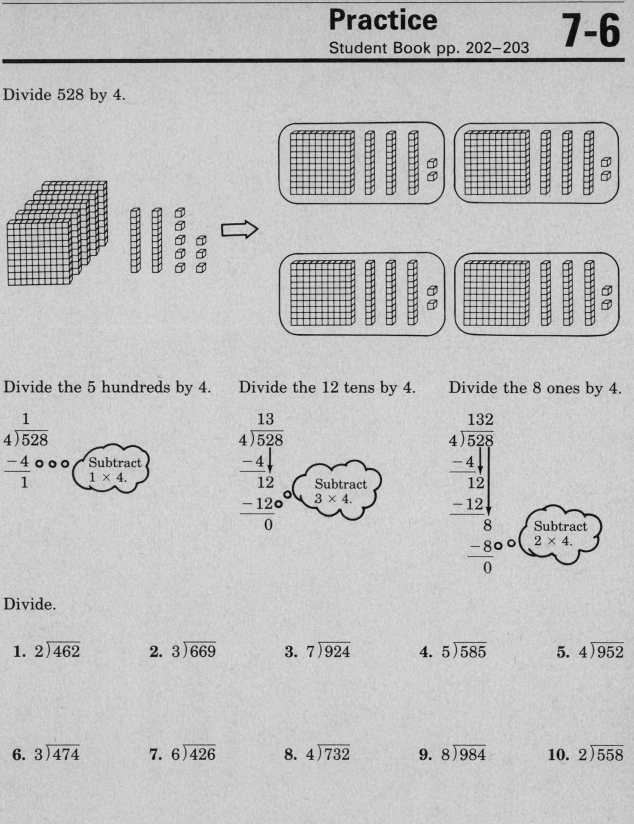

Divide the 5 hundreds by 4.

$$\begin{array}{r} 1 \\ 4)\overline{528} \\ -4 \\ \hline 1 \end{array}$$

Subtract 1 × 4.

Divide the 12 tens by 4.

$$\begin{array}{r} 13 \\ 4)\overline{528} \\ -4\downarrow \\ \hline 12 \\ -12 \\ \hline 0 \end{array}$$

Subtract 3 × 4.

Divide the 8 ones by 4.

$$\begin{array}{r} 132 \\ 4)\overline{528} \\ -4\downarrow \\ \hline 12 \\ -12\downarrow \\ \hline 8 \\ -8 \\ \hline 0 \end{array}$$

Subtract 2 × 4.

Divide.

1. 2)462   **2.** 3)669   **3.** 7)924   **4.** 5)585   **5.** 4)952

6. 3)474   **7.** 6)426   **8.** 4)732   **9.** 8)984   **10.** 2)558

11. 5)925   **12.** 7)812   **13.** 2)122   **14.** 6)786   **15.** 4)864

Practice

Student Book pp. 204–205

Divide 832 by 8.

Divide the hundreds by 8.   Divide the tens by 8.   Divide the ones by 8.

$$\begin{array}{r} 1 \\ 8\overline{)832} \\ -8 \\ \hline 0 \end{array}$$ Subtract 1 × 8.

$$\begin{array}{r} 10 \\ 8\overline{)832} \\ -8\downarrow \\ \hline 3 \\ -0 \\ \hline 3 \end{array}$$ Subtract 0 × 8.

$$\begin{array}{r} 104 \\ 8\overline{)832} \\ -8\downarrow\downarrow \\ \hline 3 \\ -0\downarrow \\ \hline 32 \\ -32 \\ \hline 0 \end{array}$$ Subtract 4 × 8.

Check.

$$\begin{array}{r} 3 \\ 104 \\ \times\ 8 \\ \hline 832 \end{array}$$

Divide.

1. $3\overline{)91}$ **2.** $6\overline{)62}$ **3.** $2\overline{)41}$ **4.** $8\overline{)86}$ **5.** $4\overline{)83}$

6. $7\overline{)742}$ **7.** $3\overline{)990}$ **8.** $8\overline{)856}$ **9.** $2\overline{)480}$ **10.** $4\overline{)412}$

11. $3\overline{)915}$ **12.** $6\overline{)648}$ **13.** $5\overline{)540}$ **14.** $2\overline{)520}$ **15.** $7\overline{)714}$

Solve.

16. A scout troop decorated 654 fruit cups. The fruit cups will
be used on meal trays at 6 local hospitals. If each hospital
receives the same number of cups, how many cups will
each receive? _____

Practice

Student Book pp. 206–207

7-8

To divide $5 by 4, write $5 as $5.00 and put the dollar sign and decimal point in the quotient.

$$\frac{\$\ \ .\ \ \ \ }{4)\$5.00}$$

Divide 5 by 4.

$$\begin{array}{r} \$1. \\ 4\overline{)\$5.00} \\ -4 \\ \hline 1 \end{array}$$
Subtract 1 × 4.

Divide 10 by 4.

$$\begin{array}{r} \$1.2 \\ 4\overline{)\$5.00} \\ -4\downarrow \\ \hline 1\ 0 \\ -8 \\ \hline 2 \end{array}$$
Subtract 2 × 4.

Divide 20 by 4.

$$\begin{array}{r} \$1.25 \\ 4\overline{)\$5.00} \\ -4\downarrow \\ \hline 1\ 0 \\ -8\downarrow \\ \hline 20 \\ -20 \\ \hline 0 \end{array}$$
Subtract 5 × 4.

Divide. Remember the dollar sign and decimal point.

1. $5)\overline{\$5.45}$ **2.** $4)\overline{\$9.72}$ **3.** $5)\overline{\$7.20}$ **4.** $6)\overline{\$7.92}$ **5.** $3)\overline{\$8.73}$

6. $4)\overline{\$7.68}$ **7.** $2)\overline{\$8.12}$ **8.** $3)\overline{\$5.34}$ **9.** $7)\overline{\$9.94}$ **10.** $6)\overline{\$9.78}$

Divide. Write the quotient in dollars and cents.

11. $2)\overline{\$9}$ **12.** $4)\overline{\$7}$ **13.** $2)\overline{\$5}$ **14.** $5)\overline{\$6}$ **15.** $4)\overline{\$8}$

Use estimation, mental math, or paper and pencil to solve the problem. Write *e, m,* or *p* to tell the method you chose.

16. The drug store is selling paperback books priced at 3 for $7. Hilary has $2. Does she have enough money to buy one paperback book? _____

Divide 745 by 6.

Divide the hundreds by 6.

$$
\begin{array}{r}
1 \\
6\overline{)745} \\
-6 \\
\hline
1
\end{array}
$$
Subtract 1 × 6.

Is 1 less than 6? Yes

Divide the tens by 6.

$$
\begin{array}{r}
12 \\
6\overline{)745} \\
-6\downarrow \\
\hline
14 \\
-12 \\
\hline
2
\end{array}
$$
Subtract 2 × 6.

Is 2 less than 6? Yes

Divide the ones by 6.

$$
\begin{array}{r}
124\ R1 \\
6\overline{)745} \\
-6\downarrow\downarrow \\
\hline
14 \\
-12\downarrow \\
\hline
25 \\
-24 \\
\hline
1
\end{array}
$$
Subtract 4 × 6.

Is 1 less than 6? Yes

Divide.

1. $3\overline{)415}$

2. $6\overline{)968}$

3. $5\overline{)572}$

4. $2\overline{)457}$

5. $4\overline{)737}$

6. $3\overline{)473}$

7. $4\overline{)856}$

8. $5\overline{)658}$

9. $2\overline{)739}$

10. $3\overline{)824}$

11. $4\overline{)709}$

12. $3\overline{)622}$

13. $8\overline{)737}$

14. $5\overline{)771}$

15. $2\overline{)865}$

Solve.

16. Mrs. Salazar is a zoo keeper in charge of the monkeys. She has 365 bananas. She feeds each monkey 2 bananas in the morning. How many monkeys can she feed this morning?

_____

17. There are 181 monkeys at the zoo. Each monkey is fed 3 bananas a day plus other fruits. How many bananas are needed each day?

_____

Name

Practice 7-10

Student Book pp. 210–211

The chart at the right shows the daily low temperatures in Texas during one week in July.

Day	Low Temperature
Sunday	18°C
Monday	15°C
Tuesday	23°C
Wednesday	31°C
Thursday	32°C
Friday	28°C
Saturday	28°C

Finding the average low temperature takes two steps.

Add the temperatures.

$$\begin{array}{r} 18 \\ 15 \\ 23 \\ 31 \\ 32 \\ 28 \\ +28 \\ \hline 175 \end{array}$$

Divide the sum by the number of days.

$$\begin{array}{r} 25 \leftarrow \text{Average} \\ 7\overline{)175} \\ -14\downarrow \\ \hline 35 \\ -35 \\ \hline 0 \end{array}$$

The average low temperature was 25°C.

Find the average.

1. 6, 8, 10, 4 ______

2. 13, 11, 15, 9 ______

3. 14, 10, 12, 4 ______

4. 12, 14, 10, 8 ______

5. 11, 16, 13, 15, 5 ______

6. 9, 8, 10, 7, 11 ______

7. 20, 25, 15, 18, 22 ______

8. 36, 48, 24, 70, 42 ______

9. 152, 138, 251, 72, 127 ______

10. 92, 80, 78, 90, 81, 95 ______

11. 12, 15, 14, 11, 21, 13, 19 ______

12. 22, 17, 13, 18, 20 ______

Line graphs show changes. This graph shows the number of baseball cards sold during the baseball season. The bottom of the graph shows the months of the baseball season. The left side shows the number of cards sold at a hobby store.

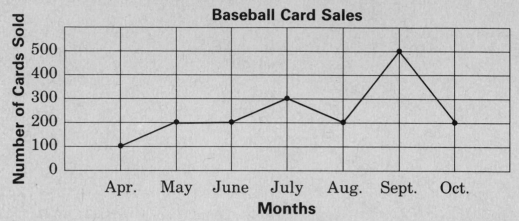

Baseball Card Sales

The graph shows that sales increased in May, July, and September.

Use the graph above to answer the questions.

How many cards were sold during this month?

1. April _____ **2.** May _____ **3.** June _____

4. July _____ **5.** August _____ **6.** September _____

7. Two months each showed decreases in sales from the last months. Which two were they? _____ _____

8. How many more cards were sold during July than during June? _____

9. Between which two months did sales increase the most? _____ _____

10. During which two months did sales remain the same? _____ _____

11. How many baseball cards were sold during the last three months of the baseball season? _____

12. What were the average sales for a month during the last three months of the baseball season? _____

13. What were the average sales for a month during the first four months of the baseball season? _____

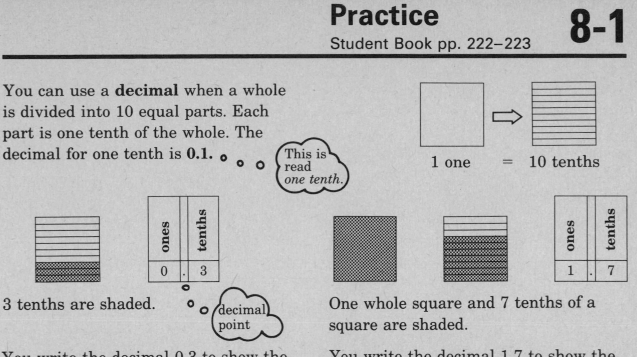

You can use a **decimal** when a whole is divided into 10 equal parts. Each part is one tenth of the whole. The decimal for one tenth is **0.1.**

This is read *one tenth.*

1 one = 10 tenths

ones	tenths
0 .	3

3 tenths are shaded.

decimal point

You write the decimal 0.3 to show the part that is shaded. You read the decimal as three tenths.

ones	tenths
1 .	7

One whole square and 7 tenths of a square are shaded.

You write the decimal 1.7 to show the part that is shaded. You read the decimal as one and seven tenths.

Write a decimal for the shaded part.

1. _____

2. _____

3. _____

Write the decimal.

4.

ones	tenths
0 .	4

_____

5.

ones	tenths
0 .	9

_____

6.

ones	tenths
2 .	5

_____

7.

tens	ones	tenths
4	1 .	1

_____

8. 3 tenths _____

9. 1 tenth _____

10. 5 tenths _____

11. 2 and 4 tenths _____

12. 7 and 5 tenths _____

13. 12 and 9 tenths _____

14. four tenths _____

15. nine tenths _____

16. eight tenths _____

Use a centimeter ruler that shows tenths of centimeters. Measure to the nearest tenth of a centimeter.

17. _____

18. _____

Practice
Student Book pp. 224–225

8-2

You can use a decimal when a whole is divided into 100 equal parts. Each part is 1 hundredth.

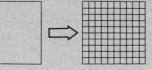

1 one = 100 hundredths

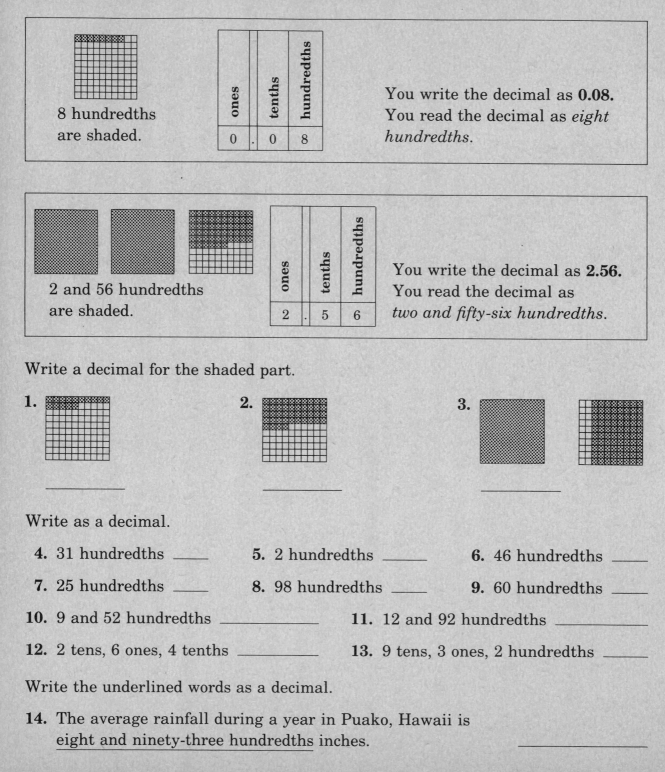

8 hundredths are shaded.

ones	tenths	hundredths
0 .	0	8

You write the decimal as **0.08**. You read the decimal as *eight hundredths*.

2 and 56 hundredths are shaded.

ones	tenths	hundredths
2 .	5	6

You write the decimal as **2.56**. You read the decimal as *two and fifty-six hundredths*.

Write a decimal for the shaded part.

1. _____

2. _____

3. _____

Write as a decimal.

4. 31 hundredths _____   5. 2 hundredths _____   6. 46 hundredths _____

7. 25 hundredths _____   8. 98 hundredths _____   9. 60 hundredths _____

10. 9 and 52 hundredths _____   11. 12 and 92 hundredths _____

12. 2 tens, 6 ones, 4 tenths _____   13. 9 tens, 3 ones, 2 hundredths _____

Write the underlined words as a decimal.

14. The average rainfall during a year in Puako, Hawaii is <u>eight and ninety-three hundredths</u> inches. _____

Practice

Student Book pp. 226–227

0.5	>	0.2

0.32	<	0.68

Compare 8.29 and 8.23

ones		tenths	hundredths
8	.	2	9
8	.	2	3

Compare the ones. They are the same.

Compare the tenths. They are the same.

Compare the hundredths. 9 hundredths > 3 hundredths. So 8.29 > 8.23.

Write < or > to compare the decimals.

1. 0.35 _____ 0.39

2. 0.41 _____ 0.49

3. 0.36 _____ 0.63

4. 2.80 _____ 2.08

5. 7.91 _____ 7.19

6. 2.46 _____ 2.56

7. 7.05 _____ 5.07

8. 8.8 _____ 8.9

9. 65.9 _____ 59.6

Complete.

10.

0   0.01 _____ _____ 0.04

11.

2   2.1   2.2 _____ _____

12.

6.41   6.42 _____ _____ _____

13.

97.5 _____ 97.7   97.8 _____

Write the decimals in order from greatest to least.

14. 0.5, 1.2, 0.4, 1.5 _____

15. 1.9, 2.5, 0.6, 2.0 _____

16. 0.06, 0.02, 0.01, 0.09 _____

You have this amount of money in your pocket. List the coins you could have.

17. You have 60¢ but can't make change for a quarter.

_____

18. You have 40¢ but can't make change for a quarter.

_____

Practice

Write as a hundredths decimal.

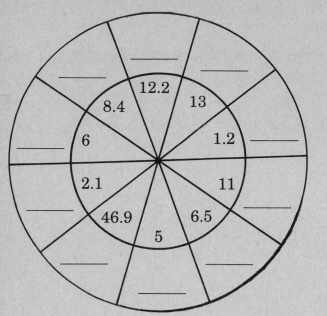

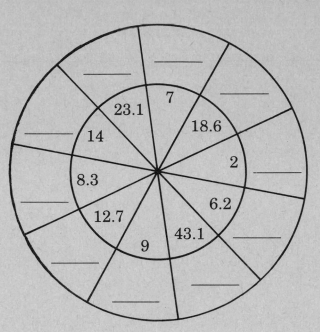

Connect the dots in order from least to greatest.

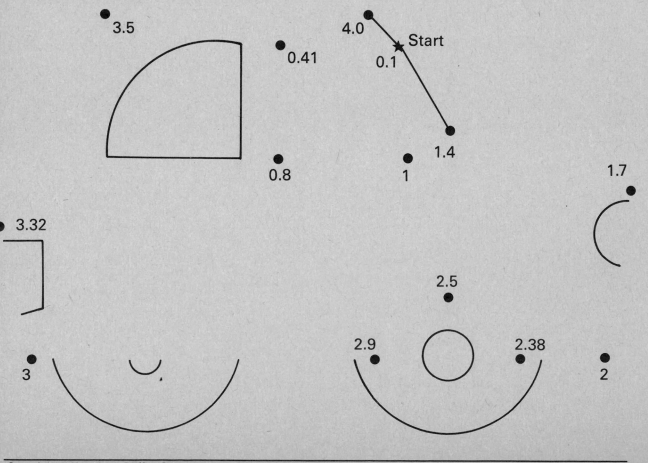

Name _____

Sometimes you don't need to know an exact number.
When that is the case, you can round the number.

The chart shows how to round numbers to the nearest whole number and to the nearest tenth.
Look at the digit to the right of the place to be rounded.
This digit tells you whether to round up or down.

Number	Round to the nearest	Digit to the Right	Is it 5 or more?	Round the number
18.25	whole number	2	no	down to 18
18.25	tenth	5	yes	up to 18.3

To round 18.25 to its greatest place value, look at the digit to the right of the ten's place. Round 18.25 up to 20.

Round to the place of the underlined digit.

1. 72.9 _____   2. 46.7 _____   3. 9.42 _____   4. 1.32 _____

5. 19.95 _____   6. 14.23 _____   7. 10.46 _____   8. 11.22 _____

9. 203.42 _____   10. 342.75 _____   11. 0.38 _____   12. 399.5 _____

13. 516.42 _____   14. 894.63 _____   15. 220.96 _____   16. 19.29 _____

Round to the greatest place value.

17. 7.2 _____   18. 28.6 _____   19. 9.51 _____   20. 8.37 _____

21. 40.60 _____   22. 26.71 _____   23. 37.25 _____   24. 64.56 _____

25. 66.10 _____   26. 348.2 _____   27. 400.29 _____   28. 251.62 _____

Use the information at the right to answer the question.

29. To the nearest tenth of a second, what was the winning time in 1980? _____

30. To the nearest whole number, in which years were the winning times about 22 seconds? _____

Olympic Winning Times Women's 200 m Dash		
1964	23.0	seconds
1968	22.5	seconds
1972	22.40	seconds
1976	22.37	seconds
1980	22.03	seconds
1984	21.81	seconds

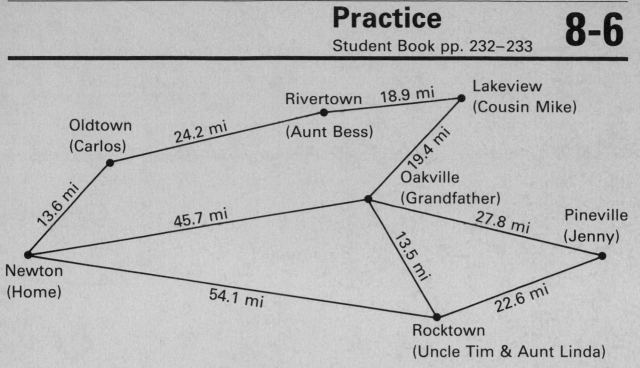

Carol is planning a trip to visit friends and family. She plans to visit Carlos, Aunt Bess, and Mike the first day. She reads her map to find that the distances between home and these first three stops are 13.6 mi, 24.2 mi, and 18.9 mi. To find about how far she will travel the first day she can estimate the total. To estimate, round each distance to its greatest place value.

$$13.6 \rightarrow 10$$
$$24.2 \rightarrow 20$$
$$18.9 \rightarrow \underline{+20}$$
$$50$$

She will travel about 50 mi the first day.

Estimate to solve.

1. The second day, Carol plans to make three more stops. The distances between the next three stops are 19.4 mi, 27.8 mi, and 22.6 mi. About how many miles will she travel the second day? _____

2. The total distance for the first day is 56.7 mi. The total distance for the second day is 69.8 mi. About how far will she drive during the first two days? _____

3. Carol plans to leave the third day from Rocktown. She will drive 13.5 mi to her grandfather's and then 45.7 mi home. About how many miles will she drive that day? _____

4. Carol's cousin, Mike, plans to follow her 19.4 mi to their grandfather's. Then he will drive 13.5 mi straight to Rocktown. About how many miles will Mike drive? _____

Practice

Student Book pp. 234–235

Cathy has two pieces of fabric. One piece measures 1.84 m long. The other piece measures 2.75 m long. How much material does she have altogether?

To find out, add 2.75 and 1.84.

Line up the decimal points.   Add.

$$2.75$$
$$+1.84$$

$$\overset{1}{2}.75$$
$$+1.84$$
$$\overline{4.59}$$

Cathy has 4.59 m of fabric.

Remember to write the decimal point in the answer.

Add.

1. 6.2 $+7.5$	**2.** 3.9 $+4.6$	**3.** 7.1 $+2.8$	**4.** 9.0 $+6.5$	**5.** 3.7 $+6.8$
6. 5.91 $+6.27$	**7.** 3.08 $+4.16$	**8.** 2.49 $+7.81$	**9.** 6.40 $+9.93$	**10.** 8.85 $+2.06$
11. 7.5 $+2.4$	**12.** 1.09 $+2.16$	**13.** 3.99 $+6.42$	**14.** 8.1 $+6.5$	**15.** 36.15 $+\ 4.28$

16. 8.16 + 2.95 = _____   **17.** 3.7 + 5.9 = _____   **18.** 16.18 + 5.23 = _____

19. 9.91 + 2.06 = _____   **20.** 14.75 + 6.79 = _____   **21.** 18.10 + 0.27 = _____

Solve.

22. Jay bought 2.96 m of upholstery. His friend Lee bought 3.47 m of upholstery. How much upholstery do they have altogether? _____

23. Jay bought 1.8 m of cord. Lee bought 1.91 m of cord. Who bought the longer piece of cord, Jay or Lee? _____

Name _____

Practice

Student Book pp. 236–237

Jon rode his bike 12.6 km on Monday. He rode it 10.8 km on Tuesday. How much farther did he ride his bike on Monday?

To find out, subtract 10.8 from 12.6.

Line up the decimal points.　　Subtract.

$$
\begin{array}{r}
12.6 \\
-10.8 \\
\hline
\end{array}
\qquad
\begin{array}{r}
\overset{1\ 16}{1\cancel{2}.\cancel{6}} \\
-10.8 \\
\hline
1.8
\end{array}
$$

Jon rode 1.8 km farther on Monday.

Remember to write the decimal point in the answer.

Subtract.

1. $\begin{array}{r} 0.8 \\ -0.2 \\ \hline \end{array}$	**2.** $\begin{array}{r} 9.6 \\ -2.2 \\ \hline \end{array}$	**3.** $\begin{array}{r} 4.8 \\ -4.0 \\ \hline \end{array}$	**4.** $\begin{array}{r} 17.5 \\ -\ 3.4 \\ \hline \end{array}$	**5.** $\begin{array}{r} 46.7 \\ -14.3 \\ \hline \end{array}$
6. $\begin{array}{r} 9.2 \\ -1.5 \\ \hline \end{array}$	**7.** $\begin{array}{r} 6.4 \\ -4.8 \\ \hline \end{array}$	**8.** $\begin{array}{r} 31.9 \\ -12.5 \\ \hline \end{array}$	**9.** $\begin{array}{r} 10.8 \\ -\ 5.9 \\ \hline \end{array}$	**10.** $\begin{array}{r} 71.4 \\ -\ 6.9 \\ \hline \end{array}$

11. $0.26 - 0.12 =$ _____　　**12.** $8.49 - 5.37 =$ _____

13. $4.50 - 2.75 =$ _____　　**14.** $46.37 - 20.21 =$ _____

15. $85.80 - 14.86 =$ _____　　**16.** $26.53 - 4.21 =$ _____

17. $19.63 - 8.75 =$ _____　　**18.** $36.95 - 0.99 =$ _____

Solve.

19. Diane left to deliver papers at 6:00 A.M. The temperature was 18.2°C. When she finished at 8:00 A.M. the temperature was 20.3°C. How much had the temperature risen in two hours?

_____

20. Crystal covers her paper route on foot. She walks 3.6 km on weekdays and 4.3 km on Sundays. How much farther does she walk on Sunday? _____

Name _____

Subtract 2.34 from 8.9.

Line up the decimal points.	Write a zero in the hundredths' place.	Subtract.
8.9 − 2.34	8.90 − 2.34	8 10 8.9̸0̸ − 2.34 6.56

Add 13 and 2.16.		Subtract 4.2 from 19.

13   13.00
+ 2.16 + 2.16
      15.16
	Write a decimal point and any zeros you need.	8 10
		19 1̸9̸.0̸
		− 4.2 − 4.2
		     14.8

Add or subtract.

1. 3.61
  + 4

2. 7.91
  − 5.2

3. 3
  + 8.2

4. 7.8
  − 2

5. 9.86
  + 1.4

6. 17.5
  − 9.72

7. 18.6
  − 13.24

8. 7.8
  + 5.25

9. 19.22
  + 3.4

10. 32
  − 12.5

11. 7.99
  + 5.1

12. 18
  − 9.8

13. 21
  − 15.7

14. 29.23
  − 24.8

15. 29.5
  − 15.64

16. 7.5 + 8 = _____

17. 7.2 − 4.16 = _____

18. 16 − 9.4 = _____

19. 27 + 31.5 = _____

20. 13 + 26.81 = _____

21. 7.60 − 3 = _____

Solve.

22. Eric spent $1.25 for a salad, $2 for a sandwich, and $.75 for a glass of milk. How much more was the sandwich than the salad? _____

23. Ashley's lunch costs $2.45. She gave the clerk $3. Using the fewest coins possible, what is Ashley's change? _____

_____

Practice

Student Book pp. 240–241 **8-10**

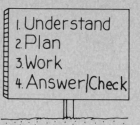

1. Understand
2. Plan
3. Work
4. Answer/Check

Leta's Juice Bar sells small cans of juice. On a chart, she kept a tally of how much juice she sold in one week.

Tally Of Cans Of Juice Sold

Kinds of Juice	Monday	Tuesday	Wednesday	Thursday	Friday
Apple Juice	III	ЖН	II	ЖН III	IIII
Orange Juice	II	ЖН I	III	ЖН	ЖН

Leta sells the apple juice for $.25 a can. She sells the orange juice for $.50 a can. Use Leta's tally to complete the chart.

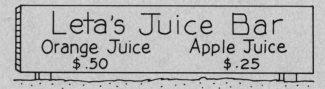

Leta's Juice Bar
Orange Juice   Apple Juice
$.50 $.25

	Days of the Week	Apple Juice	Orange Juice	Total
	Monday	$.75	$1.00	$1.75
1.	Tuesday			
2.	Wednesday			
3.	Thursday			
4.	Friday			

Use the chart to answer these questions.

5. On which day did Leta sell the most orange juice? _____

6. On which day did Leta sell the most apple juice? _____

7. During the entire week, how much money did Leta earn selling apple juice? _____

8. During the entire week, how much money did Leta earn selling orange juice? _____

9. On which day did Leta make the most money? _____

   How much did she make? _____

10. During the entire week, how much money did Leta make selling juice? _____

Practice

Student Book pp. 250–251

9-1

point *A*	• *A*	*A* is a **point**.
line *BC* or line *CB*		A **line** has no endpoints. It goes on and on in both directions. *B* and *C* are points on the line.
segment *EF* or segment *FE*		A line **segment** is part of a line. It has two endpoints. *E* and *F* are endpoints.
ray *GH*		A **ray** is part of a line. A ray has one endpoint and goes on and on in one direction. *G* is an endpoint. *H* is a point on the ray.

Name the figure.

1. _____

2. _____

3. _____

4. _____

5. _____

6. _____

7. _____

8. _____

9. _____

10. _____

11. _____

12. _____

Draw and label the segment, line, or ray.

13. line *MN*

14. ray *ST*

15. line segment *PQ*

16. line *LM*

Use mental math or paper and pencil to solve. Write *m* or *p*.

17. The lane lines on the bottom of a swimming pool are line segments. If each segment is 20 m long, how long are 8 segments? _____

Name _____

Practice

9-2

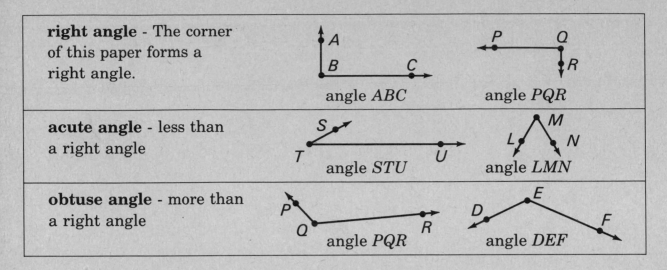

right angle - The corner of this paper forms a right angle.	angle *ABC*	angle *PQR*
acute angle - less than a right angle	angle *STU*	angle *LMN*
obtuse angle - more than a right angle	angle *PQR*	angle *DEF*

Name the angle. Then write *R* for right, *A* for acute or *O* for obtuse.

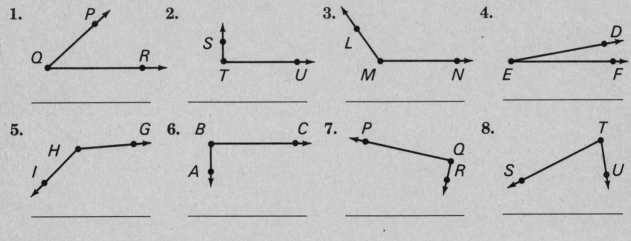

1. _____ 2. _____ 3. _____ 4. _____

5. _____ 6. _____ 7. _____ 8. _____

Draw and label the figure.

9. right angle *BCD*

10. acute angle *XYZ*

11. obtuse angle *STU*

12. line *AB*

Use the picture to answer the questions.

13. Name 5 right angles.

_____

14. Name 2 acute angles.

_____

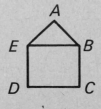

Practice

Student Book pp. 254–255

9-3

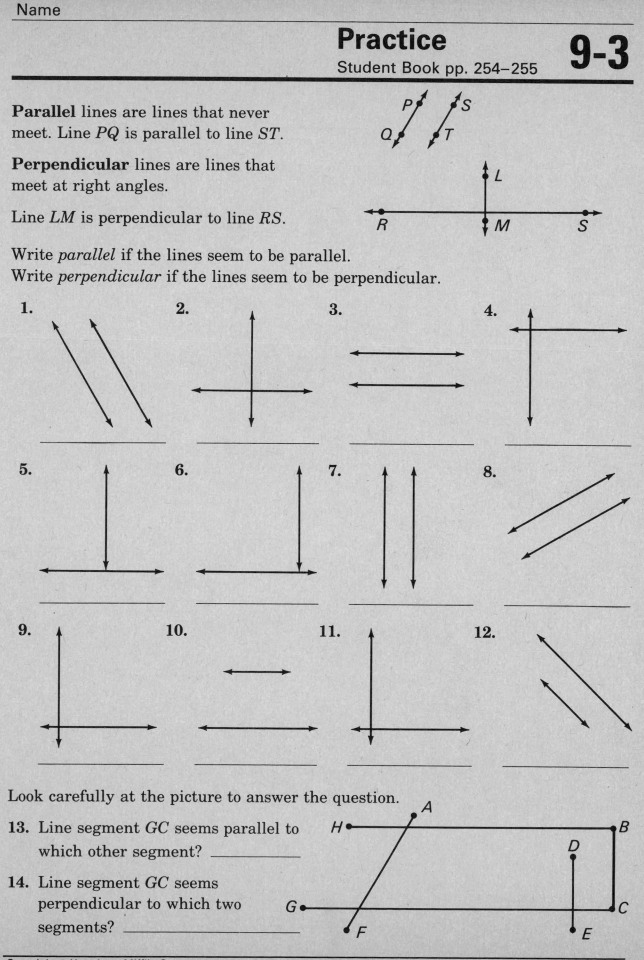

Parallel lines are lines that never meet. Line *PQ* is parallel to line *ST*.

Perpendicular lines are lines that meet at right angles.

Line *LM* is perpendicular to line *RS*.

Write *parallel* if the lines seem to be parallel.
Write *perpendicular* if the lines seem to be perpendicular.

1. _____

2. _____

3. _____

4. _____

5. _____

6. _____

7. _____

8. _____

9. _____

10. _____

11. _____

12. _____

Look carefully at the picture to answer the question.

13. Line segment *GC* seems parallel to which other segment? _____

14. Line segment *GC* seems perpendicular to which two segments? _____

Practice

Student Book pp. 256–257

Grids can help you find places on maps.

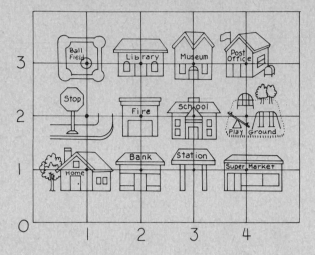

The firehouse is located at point (2,2). To find the firehouse, go 2 spaces across and 2 spaces up.

When you locate points on a grid, you start at (0, 0). Count across first and then count up.

Use the grid above. Name the place at the point.

1. (1,3) _____   2. (3,2) _____   3. (2,1) _____

4. (1,2) _____   5. (3,3) _____   6. (4,1) _____

7. (3,1) _____   8. (2,3) _____   9. (4,2) _____

10. (4,3) _____   11. (2,2) _____   12. (1,1) _____

Use the grid. Complete.

13. Carrot is at _____

14. Cheese is at _____

15. Apple is at _____

16. Soup is at _____

17. Milk is at _____

18. Bread is at _____

19. Dog food is at _____

20. Juice is at _____

MARKET MAP

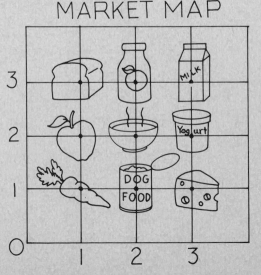

Practice

Student Book pp. 258–259

The diagram shows how birds, eagles, and doves belong together.

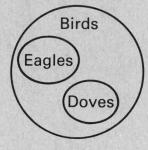

A. **All** doves are birds.

B. **Some** birds are doves.

C. **No** doves are eagles.

D. **All** eagles are birds.

Use the diagram. Write *All, Some,* or *No*.

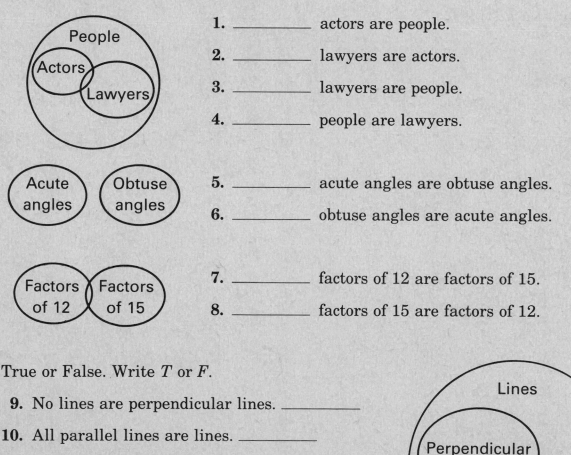

1. _____ actors are people.

2. _____ lawyers are actors.

3. _____ lawyers are people.

4. _____ people are lawyers.

5. _____ acute angles are obtuse angles.

6. _____ obtuse angles are acute angles.

7. _____ factors of 12 are factors of 15.

8. _____ factors of 15 are factors of 12.

True or False. Write *T* or *F*.

9. No lines are perpendicular lines. _____

10. All parallel lines are lines. _____

11. Some lines are perpendicular lines. _____

12. All lines are parallel lines. _____

13. Some perpendicular lines are parallel lines.

_____

14. All lines are perpendicular lines or parallel lines.

_____

Name

A **polygon** is a figure made up of three or more line segments.
The sides of the polygon meet to form angles. The points where
the sides meet are called vertexes.

These are polygons.   These are not polygons.

Types of Polygons	
triangle—3 sides	
quadrilateral—4 sides	
pentagon—5 sides	

Name the figure. Write *T* for triangle, *Q* for quadrilateral, and
P for pentagon inside the figure.

1.   2.   3.

4.   5.   6.

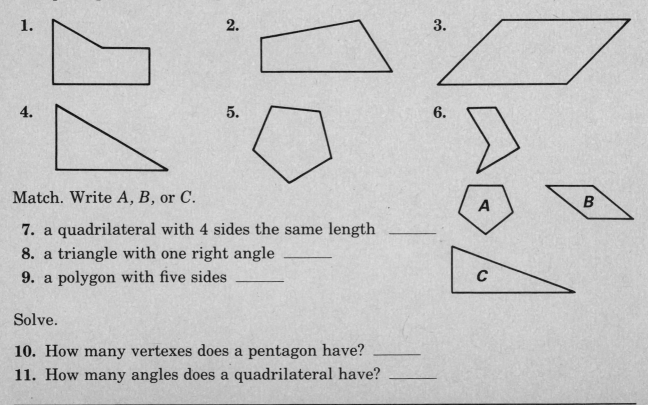

Match. Write *A*, *B*, or *C*.

7. a quadrilateral with 4 sides the same length _____

8. a triangle with one right angle _____

9. a polygon with five sides _____

Solve.

10. How many vertexes does a pentagon have? _____

11. How many angles does a quadrilateral have? _____

Special Quadrilaterals		
parallelogram	Opposite sides are parallel and the same length.	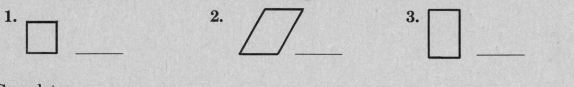
rectangle	A special parallelogram with four right angles.	
square	A special rectangle with all four sides the same length.	

Write the best name for each quadrilateral.
Write *P* for parallelogram, *R* for rectangle, *S* for square.

1. _____

2. _____

3. _____

Complete.

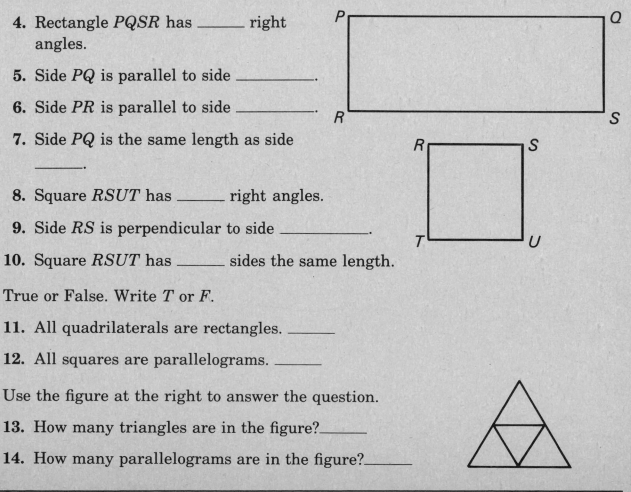

4. Rectangle *PQSR* has _____ right angles.

5. Side *PQ* is parallel to side _____.

6. Side *PR* is parallel to side _____.

7. Side *PQ* is the same length as side _____.

8. Square *RSUT* has _____ right angles.

9. Side *RS* is perpendicular to side _____.

10. Square *RSUT* has _____ sides the same length.

True or False. Write *T* or *F*.

11. All quadrilaterals are rectangles. _____

12. All squares are parallelograms. _____

Use the figure at the right to answer the question.

13. How many triangles are in the figure?_____

14. How many parallelograms are in the figure?_____

Name _____

Practice

Student Book pp. 264–265

9-8

The **perimeter** of a figure is the distance around it. To find the perimeter of a polygon, you add the lengths of the sides.

Perimeter = 6 m + 6 m + 6 m + 6 m + 6 m + 6 m + 6 m + 6 m = 48 m

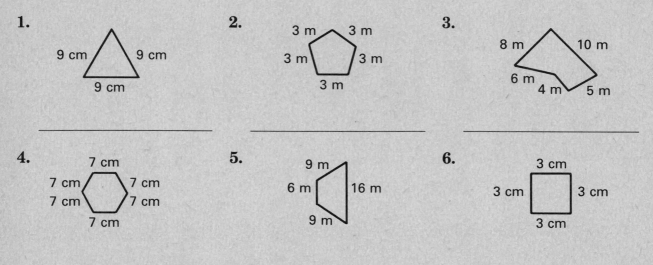

Since all the sides of this polygon are the same length, you can find the perimeter by multiplying the number of sides times the length of a side.

Perimeter = 8 × 6 m = 48 m

Find the perimeter.

1.

9 cm   9 cm

9 cm

_____

2.

3 m   3 m

3 m   3 m

3 m

_____

3.

8 m   10 m

6 m   4 m   5 m

_____

4.

7 cm

7 cm   7 cm

7 cm   7 cm

7 cm

_____

5.

9 m

6 m   16 m

9 m

_____

6.

3 cm

3 cm   3 cm

3 cm

_____

Measure the sides to the nearest centimeter. What is the perimeter?

7.

_____

8.

_____

Solve.

9. The area for a large garden is marked off with a low picket fence. The area has three sides. What shape does the fence make? _____

Practice

Student Book pp. 266–267

9-9

The **radius** is the distance from the center of a circle to the circle.

The **diameter** is the distance across a circle through its center.

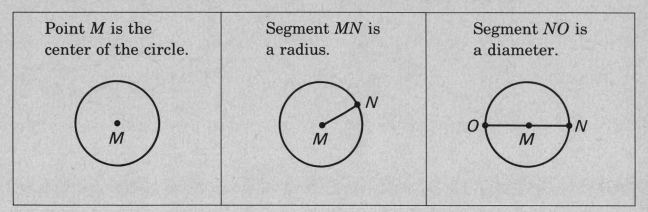

| Point *M* is the center of the circle. | Segment *MN* is a radius. | Segment *NO* is a diameter. |

Name the center, a radius, and a diameter.

1.   center _____

radius _____

diameter _____

2.   center _____

radius _____

diameter _____

3.   center _____

radius _____

diameter _____

4.   center _____

radius _____

diameter _____

True or false? Write *T* or *F*.

5. Segment *ET* is longer than segment *ND*. _____

6. A diameter of the circle is *ND*. _____

7. Angle *TEN* is an acute angle. _____

8. Angle *DET* is a right angle. _____

Draw the circle. Label the points.

9. A circle with center **A**, radius **AB**, and diameter *CD*.

Gary is planning a vegetable garden for next year. The garden will be 10 m long and 5 m wide.

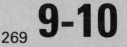

How many meters of fencing does Gary need to enclose the entire garden?

A picture helps you see that you need to add to find the perimeter of the garden.

10 m + 5 m + 10 m + 5 m = 30 m

Gary will need 30 m of fencing.

Draw a picture. Solve.

1. There will be a raised flower bed in the middle of the garden. The bed will be 2 m long and 1 m wide. Gary is going to put a fence around the flower bed. How many meters of fencing will he need? _____

2. Gary wants to put a second fence around the lettuce patch to keep the rabbits out. The lettuce patch is 3 m long and 2 m wide. How many meters of rabbit fencing will he need? _____

3. The tomato section of the garden will be 5 m long and 3 m wide. Gary wants to rope off the section so he will know where to apply tomato fertilizer. How much rope will he need? _____

4. Gary is building some boxes to shelter the young plants from the cold spring nights. Each box is made from a 1 m by 1 m wooden frame covered with a piece of heavy cloth. How many meters of wood does he need to make each frame? _____

5. A seed catalog stated that one package of flower seeds will produce a border 20 m long. Will two packages be enough for a border around the outside of Gary's garden? _____

Practice

The marching band has 4 people in each row.
There are 10 rows.
To find out how many people are in the band, multiply
4×10 or 10×4.

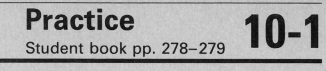

Remember: The order of the factors does not change the product.

$$\begin{array}{cc} 10 & 4 \\ \times\ 4 & \times 10 \\ \hline 40 & 40 \end{array}$$

There are 40 people in the marching band.

Use a pattern to multiply other numbers by ten.

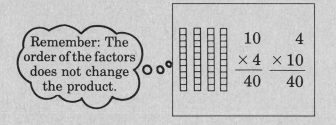

$$\begin{array}{r} 3 \\ \times 1\,\textcircled{0} \\ \hline 3\,\textcircled{0} \end{array}$$ 10 threes are 30.

$$\begin{array}{r} 1\ 2 \\ \times 1\,\textcircled{0} \\ \hline 12\,\textcircled{0} \end{array}$$ 10 twelves are 120.

$$\begin{array}{r} 1\ 2\ 5 \\ \times 1\,\textcircled{0} \\ \hline 125\,\textcircled{0} \end{array}$$ 10 one hundred twenty-fives are 1250.

Multiply.

1. $\begin{array}{r} 18 \\ \times 10 \\ \hline \end{array}$
2. $\begin{array}{r} 17 \\ \times 10 \\ \hline \end{array}$
3. $\begin{array}{r} 10 \\ \times 10 \\ \hline \end{array}$
4. $\begin{array}{r} 27 \\ \times 10 \\ \hline \end{array}$
5. $\begin{array}{r} 34 \\ \times 10 \\ \hline \end{array}$

6. $\begin{array}{r} 42 \\ \times 10 \\ \hline \end{array}$
7. $\begin{array}{r} 49 \\ \times 10 \\ \hline \end{array}$
8. $\begin{array}{r} 86 \\ \times 10 \\ \hline \end{array}$
9. $\begin{array}{r} 30 \\ \times 10 \\ \hline \end{array}$
10. $\begin{array}{r} 96 \\ \times 10 \\ \hline \end{array}$

11. $\begin{array}{r} 365 \\ \times 10 \\ \hline \end{array}$
12. $\begin{array}{r} 462 \\ \times 10 \\ \hline \end{array}$
13. $\begin{array}{r} 514 \\ \times 10 \\ \hline \end{array}$
14. $\begin{array}{r} 290 \\ \times 10 \\ \hline \end{array}$
15. $\begin{array}{r} 153 \\ \times 10 \\ \hline \end{array}$

16. $10 \times 86 =$ _____
17. $10 \times 43 =$ _____
18. $10 \times 181 =$ _____

Solve.

19. The band plays 18 different marches. Each march is 10 minutes long. If the band plays all the marches in order, how long will it take? _____

Practice
Student Book pp. 280–281

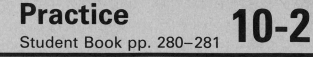

Multiply 30 × 18.
You can use 10 × 18 to help.

18		18
× 10 →three times as much→		× 30
180 →three times as much		→540

The answer is 540.

You can also use place value to find the product.

Write 0 in the ones' place.

$$\begin{array}{r} 18 \\ \times\,30 \\ \hline 0 \end{array}$$

Then multiply 18 by 3 tens.

$$\begin{array}{r} 18 \\ \times\,30 \\ \hline 540 \end{array}$$

$$\begin{array}{r} 18 \\ \times\,3\text{ tens} \\ \hline 54\text{ tens} \end{array}$$

Study this example with hundreds.

Write a 0 in the ones' place.

$$\begin{array}{r} 243 \\ \times\,20 \\ \hline 0 \end{array}$$

Multiply 243 by 2 tens.

$$\begin{array}{r} 243 \\ \times\,20 \\ \hline 4860 \end{array}$$

$$\begin{array}{r} 243 \\ \times\,2\text{ tens} \\ \hline 486\text{ tens} \end{array}$$

Multiply.

1. 64 ×10	**2.** 71 ×10	**3.** 80 ×10	**4.** 69 ×10	**5.** 84 ×30	**6.** 62 ×20
7. 48 ×40	**8.** 66 ×20	**9.** 59 ×60	**10.** 486 ×30	**11.** 629 ×70	**12.** 410 ×50
13. 864 ×30	**14.** 952 ×20	**15.** 184 ×50	**16.** 388 ×60	**17.** 435 ×40	**18.** 264 ×20

19. 27 × 30 = _____   **20.** 86 × 50 = _____   **21.** 921 × 40 = _____

Solve.

22. There are 20 ft of wrapping paper on a roll. How many

inches of wrapping paper are on the roll? _____

Practice

Student Book pp. 282–283

10-3

Sometimes you don't need to know an exact product. You can estimate the product instead.

Estimate this product.

$$824 \times 52$$

Round the numbers to the greatest place value.	824 ⟶ 800 × 52 ⟶ × 50	
Multiply.	Write a 0 in the ones' place. 800 × 50 0̤	Multiply 800 by 5 tens. 800 × 50 40,000 ∘∘∘ [800 × 5]

Round to the greatest place value to estimate the product.

1. 92
    × 34

2. 76
    × 65

3. 89
    × 28

4. 47
    × 52

5. 63
    × 18

6. 53
    × 71

7. 69
    × 21

8. 79
    × 83

9. 406
    × 52

10. 276
    × 39

11. 850
    × 25

12. 234
    × 38

13. 184
    × 68

14. 342
    × 46

15. 458
    × 32

16. 839
    × 58

17. $65 \times 34 =$ _____

18. $76 \times 82 =$ _____

19. $12 \times 31 =$ _____

20. $59 \times 625 =$ _____

21. $88 \times 246 =$ _____

22. $67 \times 931 =$ _____

Estimate to solve.

23. Each student has a math workbook with 124 pages of practice. There are 26 students in the class. About how many pages of math practice will the teacher check this school year?

_____

Practice
Student Book pp. 284–285
10-4

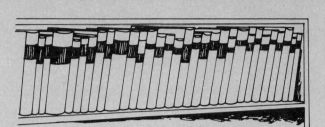

The librarian put 31 books on each shelf. There are 12 shelves. How many books are there in all?

Multiply 31 by 12. Think of 12 as 1 ten and 2 ones.

Multiply 31 by 2 ones.	Multiply 31 by 1 ten.	Add.
31	31	31
× 12	× 12	× 12
62	62	62
	310	310
		372

There are 372 books in all.

Multiply.

1. 26	2. 37	3. 49	4. 18	5. 38	6. 52
× 18	× 12	× 18	× 14	× 13	× 12

7. 92	8. 59	9. 83	10. 97	11. 21	12. 63
× 16	× 15	× 16	× 18	× 14	× 12

13. 74	14. 63	15. 75	16. 47	17. 92	18. 88
× 18	× 19	× 16	× 15	× 17	× 19

19. $19 \times 11 =$ _____

20. $85 \times 13 =$ _____

Solve.

21. The library has 12 sets of encyclopedias. Each set has 23 volumes. How many volumes are there in all?

_____

22. The librarian puts 7 magazines in each stack. There are 357 magazines. How many stacks will there be?

_____

Practice
Student Book pp. 286–287

The pet food warehouse ordered 75 cases of dog food. There are 24 cans in a case. How many cans of dog food were ordered altogether?

To find out, multiply 75 by 24.

Multiply 75 by 4 ones.	Multiply 75 by 2 tens.	Add.
$\begin{array}{r} 75 \\ \times 24 \\ \hline 300 \end{array}$	$\begin{array}{r} 75 \\ \times 24 \\ \hline 300 \\ 1500 \end{array}$	$\begin{array}{r} 75 \\ \times 24 \\ \hline 300 \\ 1500 \\ \hline 1800 \end{array}$

The warehouse ordered 1800 cans of dog food.

Multiply.

1. $\begin{array}{r} 42 \\ \times 35 \end{array}$ 2. $\begin{array}{r} 71 \\ \times 26 \end{array}$ 3. $\begin{array}{r} 83 \\ \times 48 \end{array}$ 4. $\begin{array}{r} 68 \\ \times 27 \end{array}$ 5. $\begin{array}{r} 89 \\ \times 71 \end{array}$ 6. $\begin{array}{r} 52 \\ \times 48 \end{array}$

7. $\begin{array}{r} 82 \\ \times 29 \end{array}$ 8. $\begin{array}{r} 64 \\ \times 56 \end{array}$ 9. $\begin{array}{r} 79 \\ \times 84 \end{array}$ 10. $\begin{array}{r} 59 \\ \times 48 \end{array}$ 11. $\begin{array}{r} 32 \\ \times 27 \end{array}$ 12. $\begin{array}{r} 92 \\ \times 18 \end{array}$

13. $\begin{array}{r} 75 \\ \times 43 \end{array}$ 14. $\begin{array}{r} 96 \\ \times 28 \end{array}$ 15. $\begin{array}{r} 62 \\ \times 54 \end{array}$ 16. $\begin{array}{r} 53 \\ \times 42 \end{array}$ 17. $\begin{array}{r} 45 \\ \times 68 \end{array}$ 18. $\begin{array}{r} 98 \\ \times 27 \end{array}$

Solve.

19. The dog food boxes are in rows of 26. There are 22 rows of boxes on the shelf. How many boxes in all? _____

20. The cat food cans are stacked in rows of 9. An order of 288 cans needs to be stacked in the warehouse. How many rows of cans will there be? _____

Practice

Student Book pp. 288–289

10-6

Bruce bikes 2 mi on the first day, 4 mi on the second day, and 6 mi on the third day. If he continues this pattern, how far will he go on the sixth day?

Use a chart to continue the pattern.

Day	1	2	3	4	5	6
Miles	2	4	6	8	10	12

He will go 12 mi on the sixth day.

Solve. Look for a pattern. Use a chart if needed.

1. Donna bikes 1 mi on the first day, 3 mi on the second day, and 5 mi on the third day. If the pattern continues, how far will she bike on the seventh day? _____

2. Jo is training for a long race. She runs 3 mi the first day, 2 mi the second day, 3 mi the third day, 4 mi the fourth day, 3 mi the fifth day, and 6 mi the sixth. If this pattern continues, how far will she run on the tenth day?

   _____

3. Bill is saving money to buy gifts. He saves $.30 the first week, $.70 the second week, $1.10 the third week, and $1.50 the fourth week. If this pattern continues, how much will he save the seventh week? _____

4. A display of cards will be 9 rows high. There will be 12 cards in the first row, 11 cards in the second, 12 in the third row, and 10 cards in the fourth row. How many cards will be in the last row? _____

Practice
Student Book pp. 290–291

A ferry boat can carry 235 passengers. It makes 18 trips each day. How many people can it carry in one day?

To find the answer multiply 235 by 18. Think of 18 as 1 ten and 8 ones.

Multiply 235 by 8 ones.

```
  235
 × 18
 1880
```

Multiply 235 by 1 ten.

```
  235
 × 18
 1880
 2350
```

Add.

```
  235
 × 18
 1880
 2350
 4230
```

The ferry boat can carry 4230 passengers each day.

Multiply.

1. 758 ×18	2. 394 ×16	3. 456 ×12	4. 787 ×15	5. 692 ×11	6. 829 ×14
7. 929 ×15	8. 863 ×13	9. 291 ×16	10. 758 ×17	11. 934 ×19	12. 825 ×14
13. 916 ×15	14. 835 ×12	15. 472 ×13	16. 926 ×17	17. 852 ×19	18. 695 ×18
19. 462 ×12	20. 399 ×14	21. 497 ×13	22. 836 ×15	23. 589 ×11	24. 682 ×17

Practice
Student Book pp. 292–293

Multiply 435 by 25.
Think of 25 as 2 tens and 5 ones.

Multiply 435 by 5 ones.

$$\begin{array}{r} 435 \\ \times\ 25 \\ \hline 2175 \end{array}$$

Multiply 435 by 2 tens.

$$\begin{array}{r} 435 \\ \times\ 25 \\ \hline 2175 \\ 8700 \end{array}$$

Add.

$$\begin{array}{r} 435 \\ \times 25 \\ \hline 2175 \\ 8700 \\ \hline 10{,}875 \end{array}$$

The product is 10,875.

Multiply.

1. $\begin{array}{r} 724 \\ \times 48 \end{array}$
2. $\begin{array}{r} 981 \\ \times 29 \end{array}$
3. $\begin{array}{r} 306 \\ \times 35 \end{array}$
4. $\begin{array}{r} 475 \\ \times 52 \end{array}$
5. $\begin{array}{r} 634 \\ \times 25 \end{array}$
6. $\begin{array}{r} 793 \\ \times 42 \end{array}$

7. $\begin{array}{r} 854 \\ \times 37 \end{array}$
8. $\begin{array}{r} 929 \\ \times 41 \end{array}$
9. $\begin{array}{r} 563 \\ \times 38 \end{array}$
10. $\begin{array}{r} 724 \\ \times 26 \end{array}$
11. $\begin{array}{r} 409 \\ \times 35 \end{array}$
12. $\begin{array}{r} 987 \\ \times 28 \end{array}$

13. $\begin{array}{r} 535 \\ \times 46 \end{array}$
14. $\begin{array}{r} 926 \\ \times 53 \end{array}$
15. $\begin{array}{r} 253 \\ \times 75 \end{array}$
16. $\begin{array}{r} 169 \\ \times 45 \end{array}$
17. $\begin{array}{r} 792 \\ \times 23 \end{array}$
18. $\begin{array}{r} 826 \\ \times 94 \end{array}$

19. $84 \times 263 =$ _____

20. $91 \times 405 =$ _____

Use mental math, paper and pencil, or a calculator to solve the problem. Write m, p, or c.

21. There are 24 pens in a carton. The stationery store orders 200 cartons of pens. How many pens are ordered?

_____

22. Total weekly sales for this month were $6784, $7432, $5987, and $7136. About how much were the total sales for the month? _____

There are 27 students going to the zoo.
The cost of admission is $1.25 each.
What is the total cost?

To find out, multiply $1.25 by 27.

$$\begin{array}{r} \$1.25 \\ \times 27 \\ \hline 875 \\ 2500 \\ \hline \$33.75 \end{array}$$

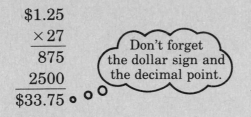

Don't forget the dollar sign and the decimal point.

The total cost of admission is $33.75.

Multiply.

1. $6.52 ×34	**2.** $7.06 ×52	**3.** $8.93 ×29	**4.** $5.75 ×18	**5.** $6.29 ×43
6. $ .95 ×29	**7.** $1.60 ×47	**8.** $3.99 ×56	**9.** $8.08 ×75	**10.** $9.45 ×39
11. $3.98 ×24	**12.** $ .85 ×79	**13.** $6.57 ×83	**14.** $7.99 ×19	**15.** $8.63 ×27

Use the information in the table to solve.

16. At the zoo, 12 students each bought a poster.
What was the total cost of the posters?

_____

17. One student bought a T-shirt and a hat. How
much did they cost altogether? _____

Souvenir Price List

Key Ring	$1.29
T-shirt	$7.49
Poster	$2.95
Hat	$4.99
Post Cards	$ .30

Practice

Student Book pp. 296–297

Use the picture to solve. Give two possible answers.
The first one is started for you.

1. Name two things you can buy if you want to spend between
$10 and $15.

   tie and sweater

2. Name two things you can buy if you want to spend between
$15 and $20.

3. Name three things you can buy if you want to spend
between $15 and $20.

4. Name two ways you can pay for two pairs of sneakers
exactly if you have 8 one-dollar bills, 3 five-dollar bills,
1 ten-dollar bill, and 1 twenty-dollar bill.

Solve. There is more than one answer.

5. You need to go to the shoe store, the bakery, and the book
store while at the shopping mall. In what order might you
go to the stores if you end up at the book store?

6. Jon needs 18 miniature lightbulbs. They are sold in
packages of 3, 4, or 5. How many packages should he buy?

Name _____

Divide 94 by 30.

Think of $3\overline{)9}$.

Write the remainder with the quotient.

$$\begin{array}{r} 3 \\ 30\overline{)94} \\ -90 \\ \hline 4 \end{array}$$ Subtract 3×30.

$$\begin{array}{r} 3\ R4 \\ 30\overline{)94} \\ -90 \\ \hline 4 \end{array}$$

Divide 126 by 30.

Think of $3\overline{)12}$. Write the remainder with the quotient.

$$\begin{array}{r} 4 \\ 30\overline{)126} \\ -120 \\ \hline 6 \end{array}$$ Subtract 4×30.

$$\begin{array}{r} 4\ R6 \\ 30\overline{)126} \\ -120 \\ \hline 6 \end{array}$$

Divide.

1. $10\overline{)52}$ 2. $40\overline{)86}$ 3. $30\overline{)99}$ 4. $60\overline{)78}$ 5. $20\overline{)85}$

6. $70\overline{)83}$ 7. $90\overline{)99}$ 8. $30\overline{)46}$ 9. $10\overline{)37}$ 10. $20\overline{)67}$

11. $50\overline{)163}$ 12. $60\overline{)368}$ 13. $80\overline{)492}$ 14. $20\overline{)147}$ 15. $70\overline{)280}$

16. $30\overline{)185}$ 17. $40\overline{)249}$ 18. $50\overline{)250}$ 19. $60\overline{)170}$ 20. $90\overline{)363}$

Solve.

21. A bus can hold 50 people. How many buses are needed to take 94 students to the show? _____

Name _____

Divide 96 by 42.

Round 42 down to 40.

Think of 4⟌9.

Write the remainder with the quotient.

40

42⟌96

40

  2
42⟌96
 −84   Subtract
 ⎯⎯⎯   2 × 42.
  12

  2 R12
42⟌96
 −84
 ⎯⎯⎯
  12

Divide.

1. 34⟌75   **2.** 27⟌91   **3.** 19⟌86   **4.** 42⟌97   **5.** 59⟌79

6. 76⟌82   **7.** 85⟌90   **8.** 32⟌98   **9.** 18⟌80   **10.** 26⟌91

11. 92⟌94   **12.** 34⟌78   **13.** 41⟌82   **14.** 29⟌97   **15.** 33⟌99

16. 28⟌186   **17.** 21⟌194   **18.** 96⟌541   **19.** 56⟌184   **20.** 61⟌244

Solve.

21. Mr. Danto is buying 96 pencils to give to his students. They cost 4¢ each. There are 32 students in the class. How many pencils will each student get? _____

22. Mrs. Lee bought 35 blue pens and 40 black pens to give to her students. There are 34 students in her class. How many pens did she buy in all? _____

Practice

11-3

Mrs. Peterson went to the post office.
She bought 8 stamps at $.22 each.
How much change did she get from $2.00?

When you solve a problem you should
think about what might be a likely
answer. Would Mrs. Peterson get back
$1.76, $.24, or $1.00?

To solve the problem, first you multiply,
then subtract.

$$\begin{array}{cc} \$.22 & \$2.00 \\ \underline{\times 8} & \underline{-\ 1.76} \\ \$1.76 & \end{array}$$

You can tell that when you subtract,
the answer will be less than $1.00, so
the most likely answer is $.24.

If the answer makes sense, write *correct*.
If it does not make sense, give the correct answer.

1. Understand
2. Plan
3. Work
4. Answer

1. Mrs. Peterson bought groceries for $86.21. She gave the
   clerk $100.00. How much change did she receive?

   Answer: $79.00 _____

2. Mrs. Peterson drove 36 km during the day. She used 4 liters
   of gasoline. How many kilometers per liter does her car get?

   Answer: 90 km per liter _____

3. Mrs. Peterson bought 3 kg of meat for $17.94. How much is
   1 kg of meat?

   Answer: $5.98 _____

4. Mrs. Peterson's total shopping bill was $86.21. She spent
   $25.32 on meat. How much did she spend on her other
   groceries?

   Answer: $111.53 _____

5. Mrs. Peterson bought a package of 6 grapefruit for $2.34.
   What is the price of 1 grapefruit?

   Answer: $2.28 _____

Name _____

Divide 962 by 40.

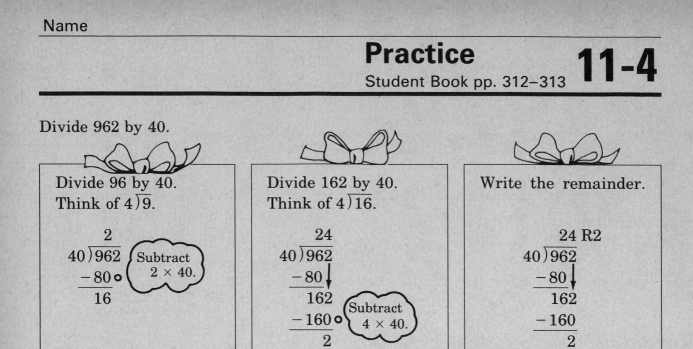

Divide 96 by 40.
Think of 4)‾9.

$$\begin{array}{r} 2 \\ 40)\overline{962} \\ -80 \\ \hline 16 \end{array}$$ Subtract 2 × 40.

Divide 162 by 40.
Think of 4)‾16.

$$\begin{array}{r} 24 \\ 40)\overline{962} \\ -80\downarrow \\ \hline 162 \\ -160 \\ \hline 2 \end{array}$$ Subtract 4 × 40.

Write the remainder.

$$\begin{array}{r} 24\ R2 \\ 40)\overline{962} \\ -80\downarrow \\ \hline 162 \\ -160 \\ \hline 2 \end{array}$$

Divide. Remember to put zeros in the quotient when they are needed.

1. 40)‾842   2. 30)‾970   3. 70)‾910   4. 90)‾993   5. 50)‾850

6. 90)‾906   7. 20)‾927   8. 30)‾905   9. 50)‾650   10. 40)‾812

11. 60)‾909   12. 30)‾846   13. 10)‾735   14. 30)‾607   15. 20)‾967

16. 50)‾515   17. 70)‾900   18. 20)‾950   19. 10)‾640   20. 40)‾807

Use mental math or paper and pencil to solve the problem.
Write m or p beside your answer to tell the method you chose.

21. There are 20 trees cut down from each acre of trees. How
    many trees will be cut down from 360 acres?   _____

Name _____

Divide 963 by 27.

Round 27 to 30.
Think of $3\overline{)9}$.

Think of $3\overline{)15}$.

Write the remainder with the quotient.

```
 30        3
○○○  27)963
         -81
          15   Subtract
               3 × 27.
```

```
 30        35
 ○○   27)963
         -81↓
          153
         -135   Subtract
           18   5 × 27.
```

```
        35 R18
    27)963
       -81↓
        153
       -135
         18
```

Divide.

1. $19\overline{)890}$ **2.** $68\overline{)960}$ **3.** $62\overline{)744}$ **4.** $26\overline{)900}$ **5.** $57\overline{)835}$

6. $87\overline{)968}$ **7.** $34\overline{)885}$ **8.** $27\overline{)935}$ **9.** $41\overline{)916}$ **10.** $79\overline{)892}$

11. $38\overline{)926}$ **12.** $52\overline{)900}$ **13.** $44\overline{)968}$ **14.** $23\overline{)970}$ **15.** $18\overline{)520}$

Solve.

16. The Jackson family traveled 324 miles on a 3-day weekend trip. What was the average distance they traveled each day?

_____

17. Mr. Jackson traveled 294 miles in city traffic. He used 14 gallons of gasoline. How many miles per gallon does his car get?

_____

117 PA

Practice

Student Book pp. 316–317

Sometimes when you divide you have to adjust the quotient.
Divide 986 by 46.

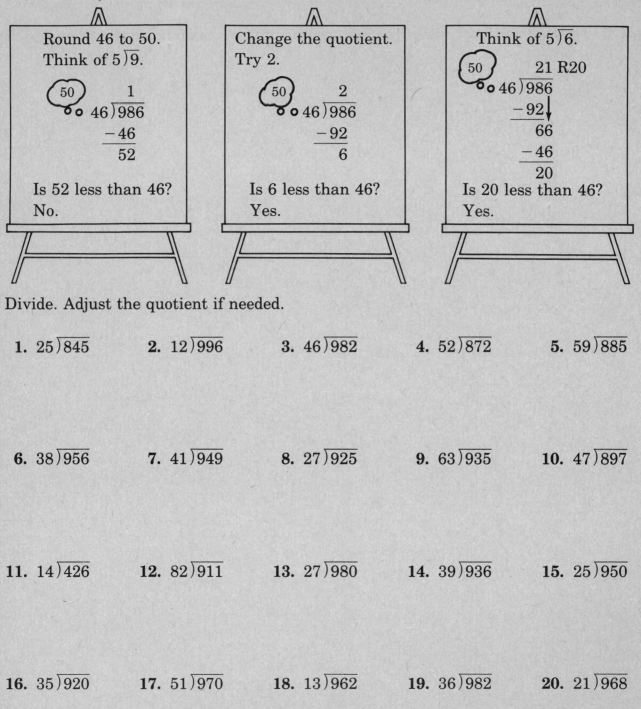

Round 46 to 50.
Think of $5 \overline{)9}$.

$$\begin{array}{r} 1 \\ 46 \overline{)986} \\ -46 \\ \hline 52 \end{array}$$

Is 52 less than 46?
No.

Change the quotient.
Try 2.

$$\begin{array}{r} 2 \\ 46 \overline{)986} \\ -92 \\ \hline 6 \end{array}$$

Is 6 less than 46?
Yes.

Think of $5 \overline{)6}$.

$$\begin{array}{r} 21 \text{ R}20 \\ 46 \overline{)986} \\ -92 \downarrow \\ \hline 66 \\ -46 \\ \hline 20 \end{array}$$

Is 20 less than 46?
Yes.

Divide. Adjust the quotient if needed.

1. $25 \overline{)845}$ 2. $12 \overline{)996}$ 3. $46 \overline{)982}$ 4. $52 \overline{)872}$ 5. $59 \overline{)885}$

6. $38 \overline{)956}$ 7. $41 \overline{)949}$ 8. $27 \overline{)925}$ 9. $63 \overline{)935}$ 10. $47 \overline{)897}$

11. $14 \overline{)426}$ 12. $82 \overline{)911}$ 13. $27 \overline{)980}$ 14. $39 \overline{)936}$ 15. $25 \overline{)950}$

16. $35 \overline{)920}$ 17. $51 \overline{)970}$ 18. $13 \overline{)962}$ 19. $36 \overline{)982}$ 20. $21 \overline{)968}$

Sometimes a problem may seem more difficult than it is because of the numbers in the problem. Rewriting the problem using easier numbers may help you see how to solve the original problem.

Original Problem

There are 810 food items to be placed on the shelves of a supermarket. If no more than 30 items can be placed on a shelf, how many shelves are needed?

Easier Problem

There are 15 items. Each shelf holds 3 items. How many shelves are needed? To find how many shelves, you would divide 15 by 3.

You can see from the easier problem that you divide.

```
       27        They will need 27 shelves.
   30)810
     -60↓
      210
     -210
        0
```

Rewrite the problem using easier numbers. Then solve the original problem.

Easier Problem

1. Peg bought $47.68 worth of food at the supermarket. How much change should she get back from $60.75?

   _____

2. The supermarket sells a package of 4 cans of juice for $1.98. Individual cans of the juice cost $.59. Which is the better buy?

   _____

3. What is the total cost of 8 canned hams at $7.75 each?

   _____

_____

_____

_____

_____

_____

_____

_____

_____

_____

Estimate 348 ÷ 7.
Use numbers that divide easily:

$$\begin{array}{r} 50 \\ 7\overline{)348} \end{array} \text{ is about } 7\overline{)350}$$

The answer is about 50.

Here's how to estimate when you have a 2-digit divisor.
Estimate 432 ÷ 67.

Round the divisor   Then think of numbers
to the nearest ten.   that divide easily.

$$67 \rightarrow 70$$

The answer is about 6.

$$67\overline{)432} \rightarrow 70\overline{)420}$$

Estimate the answer.

1. $6\overline{)319}$ 2. $4\overline{)271}$ 3. $9\overline{)206}$ 4. $3\overline{)279}$ 5. $6\overline{)287}$

6. $7\overline{)363}$ 7. $5\overline{)391}$ 8. $2\overline{)188}$ 9. $8\overline{)310}$ 10. $4\overline{)171}$

11. $37\overline{)254}$ 12. $61\overline{)370}$ 13. $67\overline{)431}$ 14. $48\overline{)257}$ 15. $78\overline{)341}$

16. $62\overline{)195}$ 17. $83\overline{)410}$ 18. $71\overline{)623}$ 19. $23\overline{)619}$ 20. $19\overline{)427}$

21. $89\overline{)921}$ 22. $42\overline{)816}$ 23. $53\overline{)521}$ 24. $12\overline{)409}$ 25. $32\overline{)615}$

Estimate the answer.

26. A case contains 48 6-oz cans of tomato juice. About how
many cases should be ordered if 490 cans are needed? _____

Practice

Student Book pp. 330–331

12-1

Write a fraction for the shaded part.

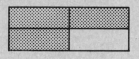

3 parts out of 4 are shaded.

You write three fourths as:

$\dfrac{3}{4}$ → numerator
→ denominator

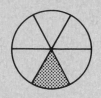

1 part out of 6 is shaded.

You write one sixth as:

$\dfrac{1}{6}$ → numerator
→ denominator

Write a fraction for the shaded part.

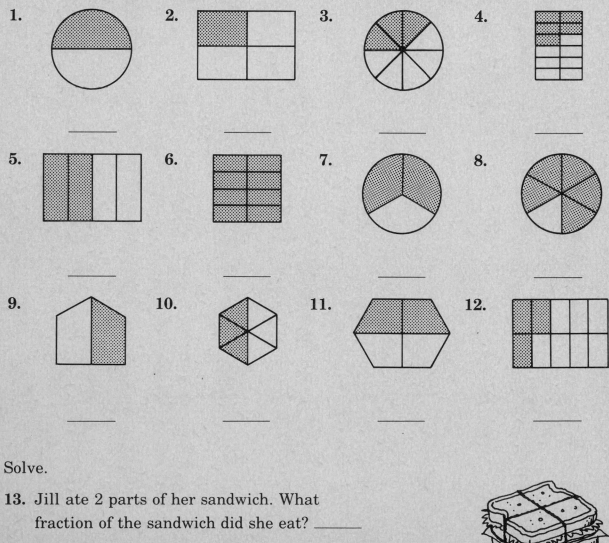

1.

2.

3.

4.

5.

6.

7.

8.

9.

10.

11.

12.

Solve.

13. Jill ate 2 parts of her sandwich. What fraction of the sandwich did she eat? _____

14. What fraction of the sandwich was left? _____

A fraction can be used to name a part of a group.

Of the five balls, 3 are soccer balls. Three fifths of the balls are soccer balls. You write $\frac{3}{5}$.

Two fifths of the balls are not soccer balls. You write $\frac{2}{5}$.

What fraction is shaded? Write the fraction.

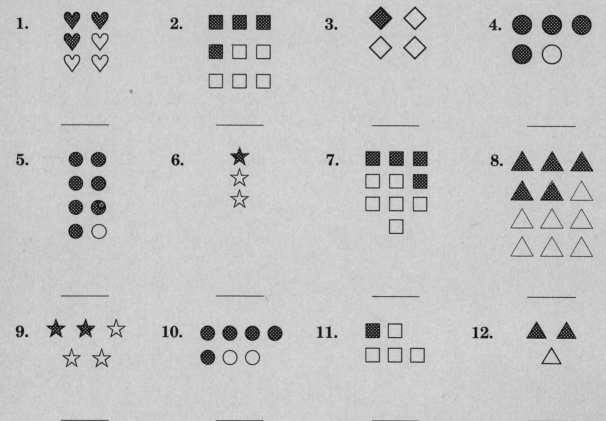

1. _____

2. _____

3. _____

4. _____

5. _____

6. _____

7. _____

8. _____

9. _____

10. _____

11. _____

12. _____

Solve.

13. Of the 15 bicycles in the bike shop, 11 are blue. What fraction of the bikes are blue? _____

14. The school soccer team won 16 games last season. The team played 25 games. What fraction of the games did the team win? _____

Name _____

This circle is cut into 4 equal parts. Two of the four parts are shaded. The fraction $\frac{2}{4}$ tells how much is shaded.

The same circle is cut into 8 equal parts. Four of the eight parts are shaded. The fraction $\frac{4}{8}$ tells how much is shaded.

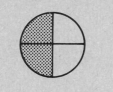

$\frac{2}{4}$ → parts shaded, → parts in all

$\frac{4}{8}$ → parts shaded, → parts in all

The fractions $\frac{2}{4}$ and $\frac{4}{8}$ name the same amount of shaded parts. They are equivalent fractions.

$$\frac{2}{4} = \frac{4}{8}$$

Write a number sentence to show equivalent fractions.

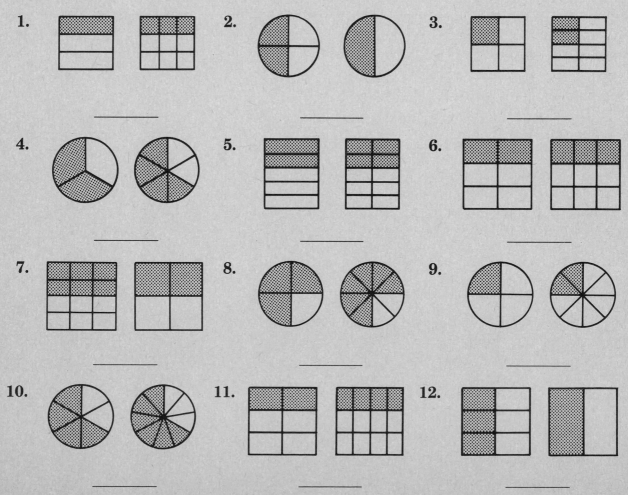

1. _____

2. _____

3. _____

4. _____

5. _____

6. _____

7. _____

8. _____

9. _____

10. _____

11. _____

12. _____

Practice

Write the fraction $\frac{12}{18}$ in lowest terms.

You can divide the numerator and the denominator of $\frac{12}{18}$ by 2.

$$\frac{12}{18} = \frac{12 \div 2}{18 \div 2} = \frac{6}{9}$$

Sometimes you can divide more than once. Divide the numerator and the denominator of $\frac{6}{9}$ by 3.

$$\frac{6}{9} = \frac{6 \div 3}{9 \div 3} = \frac{2}{3}$$

To save a step, you could have divided the numerator and denominator of $\frac{12}{18}$ by 6.

$$\frac{12}{18} = \frac{12 \div 6}{18 \div 6} = \frac{2}{3}$$

The numerator and denominator of the fraction $\frac{2}{3}$ cannot be divided by a factor greater than 1. The fraction $\frac{2}{3}$ is in **lowest terms.**

Divide the numerator and denominator by 4 to complete.

1. $\frac{8}{12} = \frac{2}{}$ **2.** $\frac{16}{20} = \frac{}{5}$ **3.** $\frac{8}{28} = \frac{2}{}$ **4.** $\frac{12}{20} = \frac{}{5}$

Divide the numerator and denominator by 5 to complete.

5. $\frac{5}{10} = \frac{}{2}$ **6.** $\frac{5}{20} = \frac{1}{}$ **7.** $\frac{15}{20} = \frac{}{4}$ **8.** $\frac{5}{30} = \frac{1}{}$

Is the fraction in lowest terms? Write *yes* or *no*.

9. $\frac{8}{16}$ _____   **10.** $\frac{9}{12}$ _____   **11.** $\frac{7}{8}$ _____   **12.** $\frac{6}{8}$ _____

13. $\frac{10}{20}$ _____   **14.** $\frac{5}{9}$ _____   **15.** $\frac{3}{10}$ _____   **16.** $\frac{6}{12}$ _____

Write the fraction in lowest terms.

17. $\frac{8}{16}$ _____   **18.** $\frac{3}{12}$ _____   **19.** $\frac{4}{12}$ _____

20. $\frac{12}{15}$ _____   **21.** $\frac{6}{10}$ _____   **22.** $\frac{4}{18}$ _____

Name _____

Practice

Student Book pp. 338–339 **12-5**

Write $\frac{10}{6}$ as a mixed number in lowest terms.

You can divide the numerator by the denominator. The remainder becomes the numerator of the fractional part. The divisor becomes the denominator.

To write the mixed number in lowest terms, you write the fractional part in lowest terms.

$$1\frac{4}{6} \leftarrow \text{remainder}$$
$$6\overline{)10} \leftarrow \text{divisor}$$
$$\underline{-\ 6}$$
$$4$$

$$\frac{4}{6} = \frac{4 \div 2}{6 \div 2} = \frac{2}{3}$$

$$\text{so } 1\frac{4}{6} = 1\frac{2}{3}$$

Sometimes fractions name whole numbers. Write $\frac{10}{5}$ as a whole number.

$$\frac{10}{5} \longrightarrow 5\overline{)10}^{\,2}$$

$$\frac{10}{5} = 2$$

Write the fraction as a mixed number in lowest terms.

1. $\frac{5}{3}$ _____

2. $\frac{10}{4}$ _____

3. $\frac{12}{5}$ _____

4. $\frac{19}{6}$ _____

5. $\frac{15}{4}$ _____

6. $\frac{11}{5}$ _____

7. $\frac{11}{6}$ _____

8. $\frac{18}{7}$ _____

9. $\frac{20}{6}$ _____

10. $\frac{15}{8}$ _____

11. $\frac{12}{8}$ _____

12. $\frac{14}{3}$ _____

13. $\frac{9}{4}$ _____

14. $\frac{10}{3}$ _____

15. $\frac{16}{6}$ _____

16. $\frac{12}{7}$ _____

17. $\frac{21}{9}$ _____

18. $\frac{28}{8}$ _____

Write the fraction as a whole number.

19. $\frac{12}{6}$ _____

20. $\frac{15}{3}$ _____

21. $\frac{9}{3}$ _____

22. $\frac{20}{10}$ _____

23. $\frac{10}{5}$ _____

24. $\frac{21}{3}$ _____

Solve.

25. Alan used $\frac{1}{8}$ teaspoon of pepper in each of the 10 omelets he made. How many teaspoons of pepper did he use in all? _____

Name _____

This ruler is marked in quarter inches.

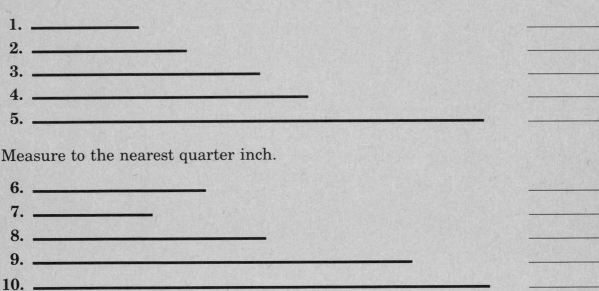

INCHES

The length of the paint brush is 4 in. to the nearest inch.

The length of the paint brush is $4\frac{1}{2}$ in. to the nearest half inch.

The length of the paint brush is $4\frac{1}{4}$ in. to the nearest quarter inch.

Measure to the nearest half inch.

1. _____   _____

2. _____   _____

3. _____   _____

4. _____   _____

5. _____   _____

Measure to the nearest quarter inch.

6. _____   _____

7. _____   _____

8. _____   _____

9. _____   _____

10. _____   _____

Draw a segment for each length. Use a ruler.

11. $2\frac{3}{4}$ in.   12. $3\frac{1}{2}$ in.

Estimate the perimeter of this figure to the nearest half inch. _____
Then measure to check.

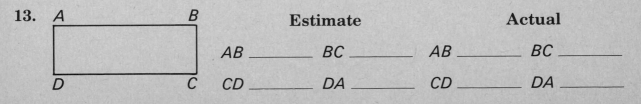

13.   A   B   **Estimate**   **Actual**

AB _____ BC _____   AB _____ BC _____

D   C   CD _____ DA _____   CD _____ DA _____

Practice
Student Book pp. 342–343 **12-7**

There are 8 pairs of socks in the drawer: 3 pairs are black, 2 pairs are brown, 2 pairs are gray, and 1 pair is white. Bob picks a pair of socks without looking. There are 8 possible results.

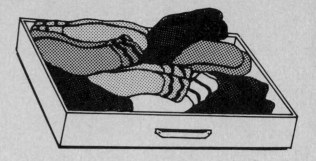

There are 2 chances that he will pick a pair of brown socks. The probability of his picking a brown pair is $\frac{2}{8}$ or $\frac{1}{4}$. There are no blue socks. The probability that he will pick a pair of blue socks is $\frac{0}{8}$ or 0.

Write the probability of picking the pair of socks from the drawer above.

1. white _____   **2.** black _____   **3.** gray _____   **4.** red _____

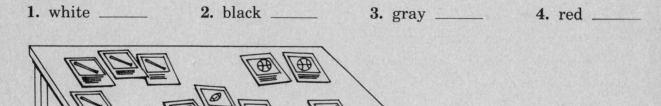

Without looking, you pick a sport card from the table above. Write the probability of picking one of these cards.

5. baseball card _____   **6.** hockey card _____

7. basketball card _____   **8.** football card _____

Solve. Write the answer in lowest terms.

9. Brenda reaches into a bag containing 6 apples. There are 3 green apples, 2 yellow apples, and 1 red apple. What is the probability that she picks a green apple? _____

10. A sporting goods store is having a drawing to give away a warmup suit. Dave registered for the drawing one time. What are his chances of winning if they have 512 entries? _____

Practice

Add $\frac{1}{4}$ and $\frac{2}{4}$.

One fourth plus two fourths equals three fourths.

$$\frac{1}{4} + \frac{2}{4} = \frac{3}{4}$$

Add.

1. $\frac{1}{5} + \frac{1}{5} =$ _____

2. $\frac{1}{5} + \frac{3}{5} =$ _____

3. $\frac{1}{6} + \frac{4}{6} =$ _____

4. $\frac{1}{8} + \frac{4}{8} =$ _____

5. $\frac{2}{8} + \frac{5}{8} =$ _____

6. $\frac{1}{8} + \frac{2}{8} =$ _____

7. $\frac{4}{10} + \frac{3}{10} =$ _____

8. $\frac{5}{10} + \frac{4}{10} =$ _____

9. $\frac{7}{10} + \frac{2}{10} =$ _____

10. $\frac{4}{12} + \frac{3}{12} =$ _____

11. $\frac{5}{12} + \frac{6}{12} =$ _____

12. $\frac{7}{12} + \frac{4}{12} =$ _____

13. $\frac{4}{9} + \frac{3}{9} =$ _____

14. $\frac{5}{9} + \frac{2}{9} =$ _____

15. $\frac{1}{9} + \frac{3}{9} =$ _____

Name _____

Practice
Student Book pp. 346–347

12-9

Add $\frac{7}{8} + \frac{3}{8}$.

Add the numerators.   Use the same denominator.   Write the sum in lowest terms.

$$\begin{array}{r} \frac{7}{8} \\ +\frac{3}{8} \\ \hline \frac{10}{} \end{array}$$

$$\begin{array}{r} \frac{7}{8} \\ +\frac{3}{8} \\ \hline \frac{10}{8} \end{array}$$

$$\begin{array}{r} \frac{7}{8} \\ +\frac{3}{8} \\ \hline \frac{10}{8} = 1\frac{2}{8} = 1\frac{1}{4} \end{array}$$

Add. Write the sum in lowest terms.

1. $\frac{1}{5} + \frac{2}{5} =$ _____

2. $\frac{1}{12} + \frac{4}{12} =$ _____

3. $\frac{1}{4} + \frac{1}{4} =$ _____

4. $\begin{array}{r} \frac{1}{3} \\ +\frac{1}{3} \\ \hline \end{array}$

5. $\begin{array}{r} \frac{2}{6} \\ +\frac{2}{6} \\ \hline \end{array}$

6. $\begin{array}{r} \frac{3}{8} \\ +\frac{2}{8} \\ \hline \end{array}$

7. $\begin{array}{r} \frac{5}{8} \\ +\frac{1}{8} \\ \hline \end{array}$

8. $\begin{array}{r} \frac{3}{10} \\ +\frac{5}{10} \\ \hline \end{array}$

Add. Write the sum as a mixed number in lowest terms.

9. $\begin{array}{r} \frac{2}{3} \\ +\frac{1}{3} \\ \hline \end{array}$

10. $\begin{array}{r} \frac{5}{8} \\ +\frac{6}{8} \\ \hline \end{array}$

11. $\begin{array}{r} \frac{5}{6} \\ +\frac{5}{6} \\ \hline \end{array}$

12. $\begin{array}{r} \frac{5}{6} \\ +\frac{4}{6} \\ \hline \end{array}$

13. $\begin{array}{r} \frac{4}{9} \\ +\frac{7}{9} \\ \hline \end{array}$

14. $\begin{array}{r} \frac{7}{10} \\ +\frac{5}{10} \\ \hline \end{array}$

15. $\begin{array}{r} \frac{4}{5} \\ +\frac{4}{5} \\ \hline \end{array}$

16. $\begin{array}{r} \frac{9}{10} \\ +\frac{6}{10} \\ \hline \end{array}$

17. $\begin{array}{r} \frac{7}{12} \\ +\frac{8}{12} \\ \hline \end{array}$

18. $\begin{array}{r} \frac{3}{4} \\ +\frac{3}{4} \\ \hline \end{array}$

Use mental math or paper and pencil to solve. Write the answer in lowest terms. Write *m* or *p* to tell which method you chose.

19. Frank jogged for $\frac{2}{3}$ of an hour on Monday. He jogged again for $\frac{2}{3}$ of an hour on Wednesday. How long did he jog in all on Monday and Wednesday? _____

20. Annie rode her bike $\frac{6}{8}$ km to the library and then $\frac{3}{4}$ km to the park. Were the two trips the same length?

_____

Subtract $\frac{5}{9} - \frac{2}{9}$. Write the difference in lowest terms.

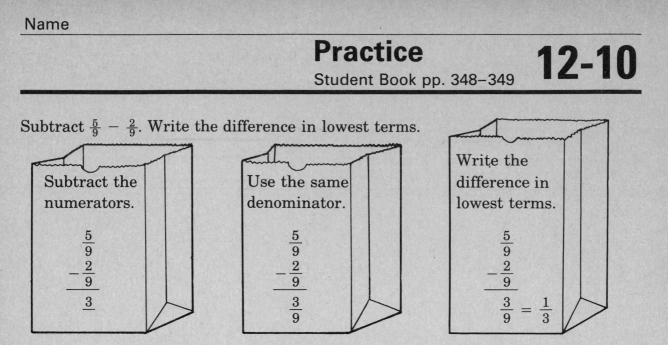

Subtract the numerators.

$$\frac{5}{9}$$
$$-\frac{2}{9}$$
$$\overline{3}$$

Use the same denominator.

$$\frac{5}{9}$$
$$-\frac{2}{9}$$
$$\overline{\frac{3}{9}}$$

Write the difference in lowest terms.

$$\frac{5}{9}$$
$$-\frac{2}{9}$$
$$\overline{\frac{3}{9}} = \frac{1}{3}$$

Subtract. Write the difference in lowest terms.

1. $\frac{7}{8} - \frac{1}{8} = $ ____ **2.** $\frac{5}{6} - \frac{3}{6} = $ ____ **3.** $\frac{9}{10} - \frac{2}{10} = $ ____ **4.** $\frac{3}{5} - \frac{1}{5} = $ ____

5. $\frac{4}{9} - \frac{1}{9} = $ ____ **6.** $\frac{7}{10} - \frac{5}{10} = $ ____ **7.** $\frac{5}{8} - \frac{1}{8} = $ ____ **8.** $\frac{4}{6} - \frac{1}{6} = $ ____

9. $\begin{array}{r} \frac{5}{8} \\ -\frac{2}{8} \\ \hline \end{array}$ **10.** $\begin{array}{r} \frac{6}{7} \\ -\frac{1}{7} \\ \hline \end{array}$ **11.** $\begin{array}{r} \frac{8}{10} \\ -\frac{3}{10} \\ \hline \end{array}$ **12.** $\begin{array}{r} \frac{4}{5} \\ -\frac{2}{5} \\ \hline \end{array}$ **13.** $\begin{array}{r} \frac{11}{12} \\ -\frac{1}{12} \\ \hline \end{array}$

14. $\begin{array}{r} \frac{9}{10} \\ -\frac{3}{10} \\ \hline \end{array}$ **15.** $\begin{array}{r} \frac{10}{12} \\ -\frac{4}{12} \\ \hline \end{array}$ **16.** $\begin{array}{r} \frac{7}{9} \\ -\frac{6}{9} \\ \hline \end{array}$ **17.** $\begin{array}{r} \frac{5}{6} \\ -\frac{1}{6} \\ \hline \end{array}$ **18.** $\begin{array}{r} \frac{9}{10} \\ -\frac{8}{10} \\ \hline \end{array}$

19. $\begin{array}{r} \frac{8}{12} \\ -\frac{6}{12} \\ \hline \end{array}$ **20.** $\begin{array}{r} \frac{5}{10} \\ -\frac{1}{10} \\ \hline \end{array}$ **21.** $\begin{array}{r} \frac{3}{12} \\ -\frac{1}{12} \\ \hline \end{array}$ **22.** $\begin{array}{r} \frac{9}{12} \\ -\frac{1}{12} \\ \hline \end{array}$ **23.** $\begin{array}{r} \frac{4}{5} \\ -\frac{3}{5} \\ \hline \end{array}$

Solve.

24. Jeff bought $\frac{3}{4}$ yd of fabric to make a costume. He only needs $\frac{2}{4}$ yd. How much extra fabric will he have? _____

25. Jean needs $\frac{7}{8}$ c of water to mix paint for the scenery. She has $\frac{5}{8}$ c of water. How much more water does she need? _____

Name _____

Practice

Student Book pp. 350–351

12-11

You can write an equivalent fraction by multiplying the numerator and the denominator by the same number.

The fraction $\frac{2}{3}$ can be written in other ways.

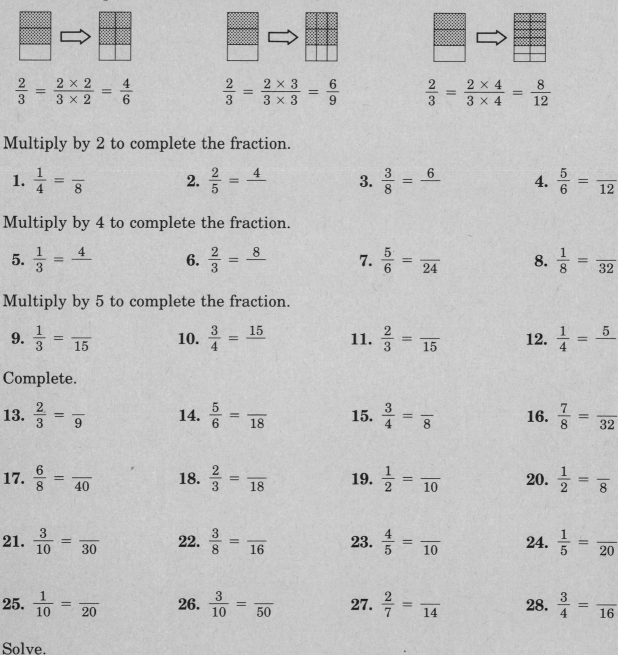

$$\frac{2}{3} = \frac{2 \times 2}{3 \times 2} = \frac{4}{6} \qquad \frac{2}{3} = \frac{2 \times 3}{3 \times 3} = \frac{6}{9} \qquad \frac{2}{3} = \frac{2 \times 4}{3 \times 4} = \frac{8}{12}$$

Multiply by 2 to complete the fraction.

1. $\frac{1}{4} = \frac{}{8}$
2. $\frac{2}{5} = \frac{4}{}$
3. $\frac{3}{8} = \frac{6}{}$
4. $\frac{5}{6} = \frac{}{12}$

Multiply by 4 to complete the fraction.

5. $\frac{1}{3} = \frac{4}{}$
6. $\frac{2}{3} = \frac{8}{}$
7. $\frac{5}{6} = \frac{}{24}$
8. $\frac{1}{8} = \frac{}{32}$

Multiply by 5 to complete the fraction.

9. $\frac{1}{3} = \frac{}{15}$
10. $\frac{3}{4} = \frac{15}{}$
11. $\frac{2}{3} = \frac{}{15}$
12. $\frac{1}{4} = \frac{5}{}$

Complete.

13. $\frac{2}{3} = \frac{}{9}$
14. $\frac{5}{6} = \frac{}{18}$
15. $\frac{3}{4} = \frac{}{8}$
16. $\frac{7}{8} = \frac{}{32}$

17. $\frac{6}{8} = \frac{}{40}$
18. $\frac{2}{3} = \frac{}{18}$
19. $\frac{1}{2} = \frac{}{10}$
20. $\frac{1}{2} = \frac{}{8}$

21. $\frac{3}{10} = \frac{}{30}$
22. $\frac{3}{8} = \frac{}{16}$
23. $\frac{4}{5} = \frac{}{10}$
24. $\frac{1}{5} = \frac{}{20}$

25. $\frac{1}{10} = \frac{}{20}$
26. $\frac{3}{10} = \frac{}{50}$
27. $\frac{2}{7} = \frac{}{14}$
28. $\frac{3}{4} = \frac{}{16}$

Solve.

29. In Jeremy's class, $\frac{6}{8}$ of the students are girls. In Jackie's class, $\frac{2}{3}$ of the students are girls. If the classes have the same number of students, does each class have the same number of girls? _____

Practice
Student Book pp. 352–353

In the bike rack, $\frac{4}{9}$ of the bikes are blue and $\frac{1}{3}$ of the bikes are red. Are there more blue bikes or red bikes?

Compare $\frac{4}{9}$ and $\frac{1}{3}$.
Write both fractions with the denominator 9.

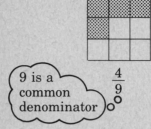 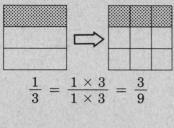 

$$\frac{4}{9}$$

9 is a common denominator

$$\frac{1}{3} = \frac{1 \times 3}{1 \times 3} = \frac{3}{9}$$

Now compare. $\frac{4}{9} > \frac{3}{9}$, so $\frac{4}{9} > \frac{1}{3}$.

There are more blue bikes than red bikes.

Compare the fractions. Write < or >.

1. $\frac{3}{8}$ _____ $\frac{4}{8}$ 2. $\frac{2}{5}$ _____ $\frac{1}{5}$ 3. $\frac{5}{6}$ _____ $\frac{1}{6}$ 4. $\frac{2}{7}$ _____ $\frac{3}{7}$

5. $\frac{0}{6}$ _____ $\frac{5}{6}$ 6. $\frac{1}{9}$ _____ $\frac{0}{9}$ 7. $\frac{7}{8}$ _____ $\frac{5}{8}$ 8. $\frac{2}{3}$ _____ $\frac{1}{3}$

9. $\frac{2}{8}$ _____ $\frac{3}{4}$ 10. $\frac{1}{2}$ _____ $\frac{3}{4}$ 11. $\frac{5}{8}$ _____ $\frac{1}{2}$ 12. $\frac{4}{6}$ _____ $\frac{1}{2}$

13. $\frac{1}{3}$ _____ $\frac{3}{6}$ 14. $\frac{5}{6}$ _____ $\frac{5}{12}$ 15. $\frac{3}{4}$ _____ $\frac{3}{8}$ 16. $\frac{2}{3}$ _____ $\frac{3}{6}$

17. $\frac{1}{2}$ _____ $\frac{4}{10}$ 18. $\frac{3}{8}$ _____ $\frac{7}{16}$ 19. $\frac{1}{6}$ _____ $\frac{5}{18}$ 20. $\frac{2}{3}$ _____ $\frac{5}{6}$

21. $\frac{2}{5}$ _____ $\frac{3}{10}$ 22. $\frac{5}{10}$ _____ $\frac{3}{5}$ 23. $\frac{1}{2}$ _____ $\frac{3}{10}$ 24. $\frac{2}{5}$ _____ $\frac{7}{15}$

25. $\frac{1}{2}$ _____ $\frac{1}{4}$ 26. $\frac{1}{8}$ _____ $\frac{1}{2}$ 27. $\frac{3}{12}$ _____ $\frac{5}{6}$ 28. $\frac{2}{4}$ _____ $\frac{3}{8}$

Write the fractions in order from least to greatest.

29. $\frac{5}{6}, \frac{1}{6}, \frac{2}{6}$ _____

30. $\frac{3}{10}, \frac{9}{10}, \frac{1}{10}$ _____

31. $\frac{6}{9}, \frac{7}{9}, \frac{1}{9}$ _____

32. $\frac{3}{6}, \frac{1}{6}, \frac{4}{6}$ _____

Name _____

Add $\frac{3}{4}$ and $\frac{10}{12}$.

Are the denominators different? Yes.

Write equivalent fractions with a common denominator.

Add the fractions. Write the answer as a mixed number in lowest terms.

$$\begin{array}{r} \frac{3}{4} \\ +\frac{10}{12} \\ \hline \end{array}$$

$$\frac{3}{4} = \frac{9}{12}$$
$$+\frac{10}{12} = +\frac{10}{12}$$

$$\frac{3}{4} = \frac{9}{12}$$
$$+\frac{10}{12} = +\frac{10}{12}$$
$$\frac{19}{12} = 1\frac{7}{12}$$

Add. Write the sum in lowest terms.

1. $\begin{array}{r}\frac{7}{8}\\+\frac{1}{4}\\\hline\end{array}$

2. $\begin{array}{r}\frac{2}{5}\\+\frac{1}{10}\\\hline\end{array}$

3. $\begin{array}{r}\frac{3}{10}\\+\frac{1}{2}\\\hline\end{array}$

4. $\begin{array}{r}\frac{1}{3}\\+\frac{1}{6}\\\hline\end{array}$

5. $\begin{array}{r}\frac{3}{8}\\+\frac{13}{16}\\\hline\end{array}$

6. $\begin{array}{r}\frac{2}{3}\\+\frac{4}{9}\\\hline\end{array}$

7. $\begin{array}{r}\frac{5}{6}\\+\frac{5}{12}\\\hline\end{array}$

8. $\begin{array}{r}\frac{4}{5}\\+\frac{1}{10}\\\hline\end{array}$

9. $\begin{array}{r}\frac{7}{10}\\+\frac{1}{5}\\\hline\end{array}$

10. $\frac{2}{5} + \frac{11}{15} =$ ____

11. $\frac{1}{4} + \frac{5}{12} =$ ____

12. $\frac{2}{3} + \frac{1}{9} =$ ____

13. $\frac{1}{10} + \frac{1}{2} =$ ____

14. $\frac{3}{5} + \frac{3}{10} =$ ____

15. $\frac{5}{6} + \frac{5}{18} =$ ____

Solve. Write the answer in lowest terms.

16. In math, $\frac{2}{3}$ of the homework problems were multiplication problems and $\frac{1}{6}$ of the problems were division problems. What part of the homework assignment was on multiplication and division? _____

Practice
12-14

Subtract $\frac{1}{4}$ from $\frac{7}{8}$.

Are the denominators different? Yes.	Write the equivalent fractions with common denominator.	Subtract the fractions. Write the answer in lowest terms.

$\begin{array}{r} \frac{7}{8} \\ -\frac{1}{4} \\ \hline \end{array}$

$\begin{array}{r} \frac{7}{8} = \frac{7}{8} \\ -\frac{1}{4} = -\frac{2}{8} \\ \hline \end{array}$

$\begin{array}{r} \frac{7}{8} = \frac{7}{8} \\ -\frac{1}{4} = -\frac{2}{8} \\ \hline \frac{5}{8} \end{array}$

Subtract. Write the answers in lowest terms.

1. $\begin{array}{r} \frac{3}{4} \\ -\frac{1}{16} \\ \hline \end{array}$

2. $\begin{array}{r} \frac{3}{4} \\ -\frac{3}{8} \\ \hline \end{array}$

3. $\begin{array}{r} \frac{5}{6} \\ -\frac{1}{2} \\ \hline \end{array}$

4. $\begin{array}{r} \frac{4}{5} \\ -\frac{2}{10} \\ \hline \end{array}$

5. $\begin{array}{r} \frac{2}{3} \\ -\frac{4}{9} \\ \hline \end{array}$

6. $\begin{array}{r} \frac{3}{5} \\ -\frac{3}{10} \\ \hline \end{array}$

7. $\begin{array}{r} \frac{7}{10} \\ -\frac{1}{5} \\ \hline \end{array}$

8. $\begin{array}{r} \frac{9}{10} \\ -\frac{1}{2} \\ \hline \end{array}$

9. $\begin{array}{r} \frac{2}{3} \\ -\frac{1}{6} \\ \hline \end{array}$

10. $\frac{2}{3} - \frac{1}{12} =$ _____

11. $\frac{7}{10} - \frac{2}{5} =$ _____

12. $\frac{3}{4} - \frac{1}{2} =$ _____

13. $\frac{5}{8} - \frac{1}{2} =$ _____

14. $\frac{3}{4} - \frac{1}{12} =$ _____

15. $\frac{1}{2} - \frac{1}{6} =$ _____

Solve. Write the answer in lowest terms.

16. Linda cut a piece of fabric that measured $\frac{5}{6}$ yd into 2 pieces. One piece measured $\frac{7}{12}$ yd long.

How long was the second piece? _____

Practice

Student Book pp. 358–359

12-15

The graph shows how Bob spends his exercise time.

Bob's Exercise Time

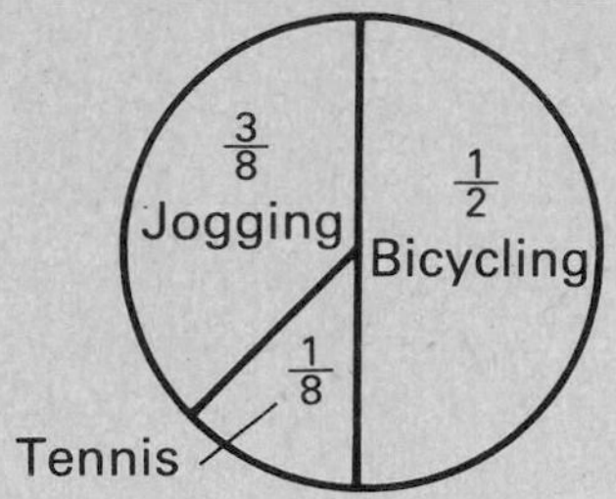

$\frac{3}{8}$ Jogging
$\frac{1}{2}$ Bicycling
$\frac{1}{8}$
Tennis

Use the circle graph to solve.

1. What does Doug do the most during his exercise time? _____

2. What does he do the least? _____

3. What fraction of his exercise time does he spend bicycling? _____

4. Does he spend more time jogging or playing tennis? _____

5. What fraction of his exercise time does he use either jogging or playing tennis? _____

Carol's class voted for their favorite sport. The graph shows the results.

Favorite Sport

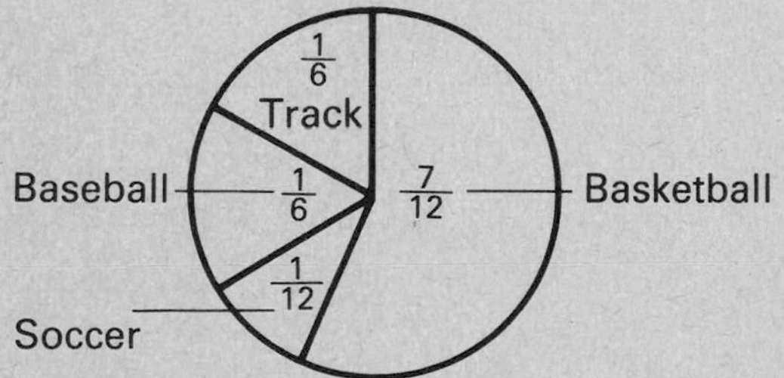

$\frac{1}{6}$ Track
Baseball — $\frac{1}{6}$ — $\frac{7}{12}$ — Basketball
$\frac{1}{12}$
Soccer

Use the graph to answer the questions.

6. Which sport received the most votes? _____

7. Which sport received the least number of votes? _____

8. What fraction of students like basketball or track best? _____

9. What is the difference between the fraction of students who chose track and the fraction of students who chose soccer? _____

10. Which is greater, the fraction of students who like basketball best or the fraction of the students who chose the other sports? _____

Practice

Student Book pp. 368–369

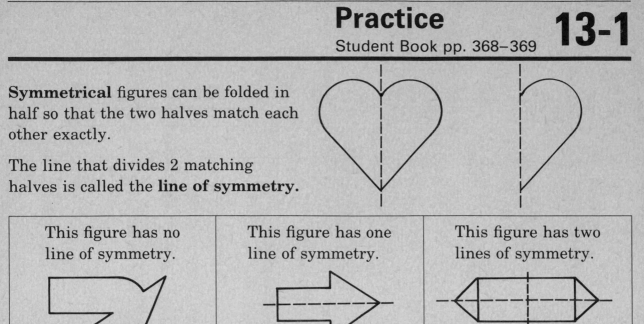

Symmetrical figures can be folded in half so that the two halves match each other exactly.

The line that divides 2 matching halves is called the **line of symmetry**.

This figure has no line of symmetry.	This figure has one line of symmetry.	This figure has two lines of symmetry.

How many lines of symmetry does the figure have?
Write *0, 1* or *2*.

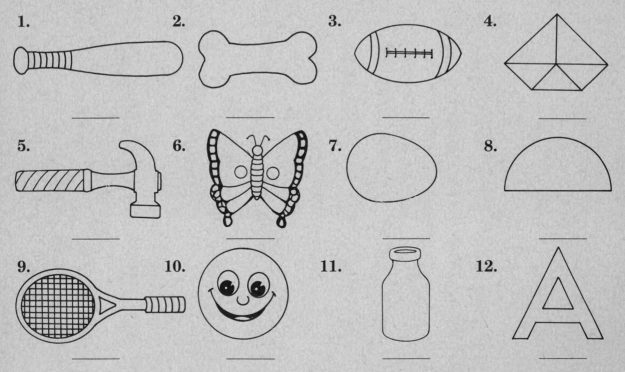

1.

2.

3.

4.

_____

_____

_____

_____

5.

6.

7.

8.

_____

_____

_____

_____

9.

10.

11.

12.

_____

_____

_____

_____

Draw the shape.

13. Draw a triangle that has only 1 line of symmetry.

14. Draw a triangle that has no lines of symmetry.

Tell whether Figure B is a slide, a flip, or a turn of Figure A.
Write *s*, *f*, or *t*.

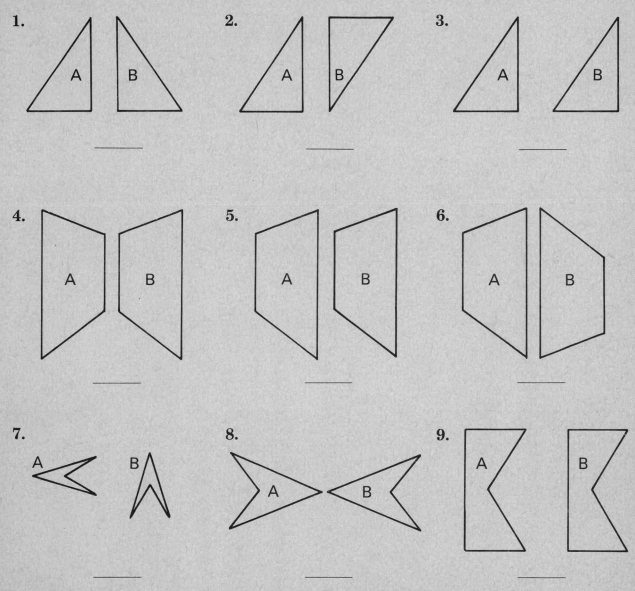

Draw the figure that shows a slide, a flip, or a turn.

10. a slide   **11.** a flip   **12.** a turn

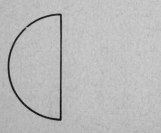  

Name _____

Practice
Student Book pp. 372–373 **13-3**

Figures are **congruent** if they have the same shape and size.

These circles are congruent.

You can slide one to fit over the other exactly.

These squares are not congruent.

They have the same shape but they are not the same size.

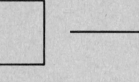

Match the congruent figures. Write the letter from the group of figures on the right.

1. _____   2. _____

3. _____   4. _____

5. _____   6. _____

7. _____   8. _____

9. _____   10. _____

11. _____   12. _____

Practice

Figures that are the same shape but not necessarily the same size are called **similar** figures.

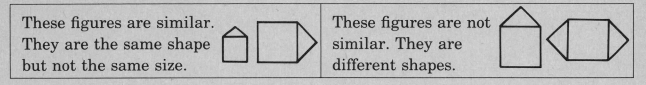

These figures are similar. They are the same shape but not the same size.

These figures are not similar. They are different shapes.

Ring the figure that is similar to the first.

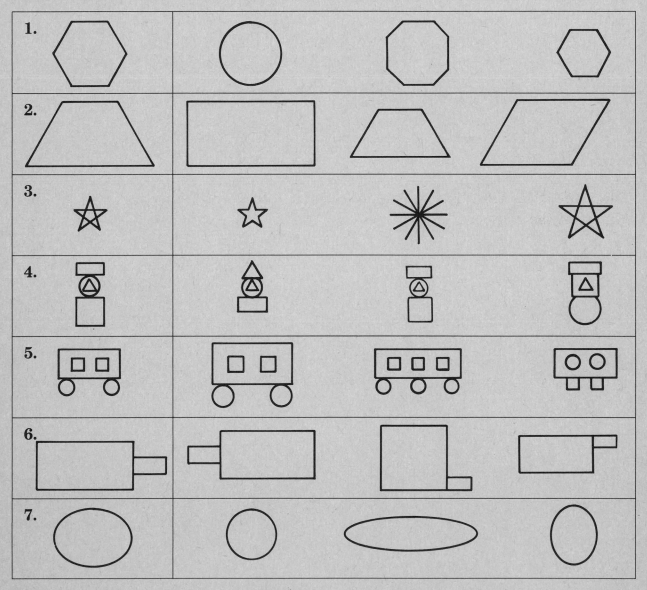

Write *All*, *Some*, or *No*.

8. _____ parallelograms are similar to each other.

9. _____ triangles are similar to quadrilaterals.

Practice

Student Book pp. 376–377

Which comes next? Ring *a* or *b*.

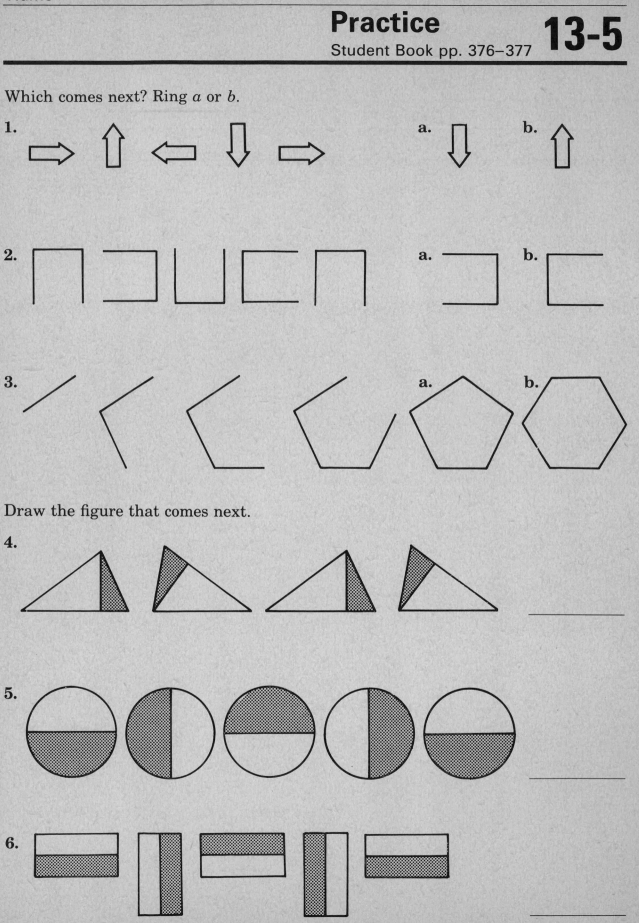

Draw the figure that comes next.

Practice

Student Book pp. 378–379 **13-6**

The area of a shape is the number
of square units that fits inside it.
Each unit is 1 square centimeter.
The area of the shape is 9 square centimeters.

Write the area of the shaded part in square centimeters.

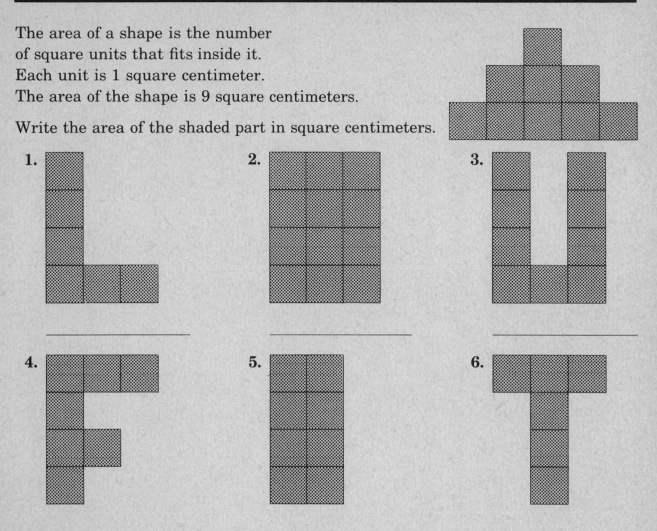

1.

2.

3.

4.

5.

6.

_____

Use the plan to solve.

7. What is the area of the couch?

    _____

8. What is the area of the piano?

    _____

9. What is the area of the chair?

    _____

10. Which piece of furniture has the
     smallest area? _____

11. Which piece of furniture has the
     largest area? _____

Family Room Plan
Each ☐ is a square unit.

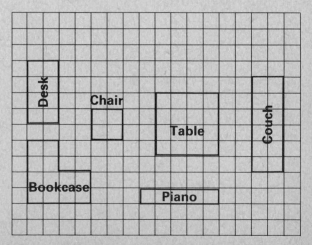

Desk
Chair
Table
Couch
Bookcase
Piano

Name _____

Mr. and Mrs. Kane are ordering carpeting for their bedroom. The room measures 5 m by 4 m. How much carpeting do they need?

To find out, you must find the area of the room.

> Area = length × width
> Area = 5 × 4
> Area = 20

Mr. and Mrs. Kane need 20 square meters of carpeting.

4 m

5 m

Find the area. Be sure to write the correct units.

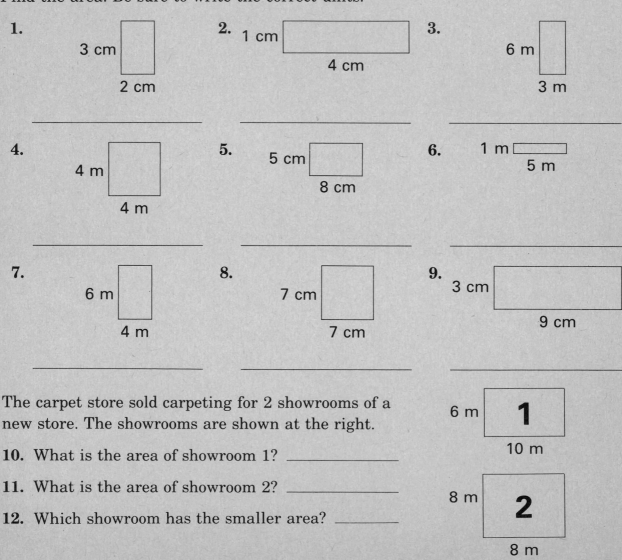

1. 3 cm 2 cm

2. 1 cm 4 cm

3. 6 m 3 m

_____   _____   _____

4. 4 m 4 m

5. 5 cm 8 cm

6. 1 m 5 m

_____   _____   _____

7. 6 m 4 m

8. 7 cm 7 cm

9. 3 cm 9 cm

_____   _____   _____

The carpet store sold carpeting for 2 showrooms of a new store. The showrooms are shown at the right.

6 m **1** 10 m

10. What is the area of showroom 1? _____

11. What is the area of showroom 2? _____

8 m **2** 8 m

12. Which showroom has the smaller area? _____

Practice
Student Book pp. 382–383

Look at the scale drawing of a porch. You can use the
scale drawing to find the area of the porch.
First count the number of squares. There are 7
squares. Then read the scale. The scale tells you that
each square stands for 4 square feet.

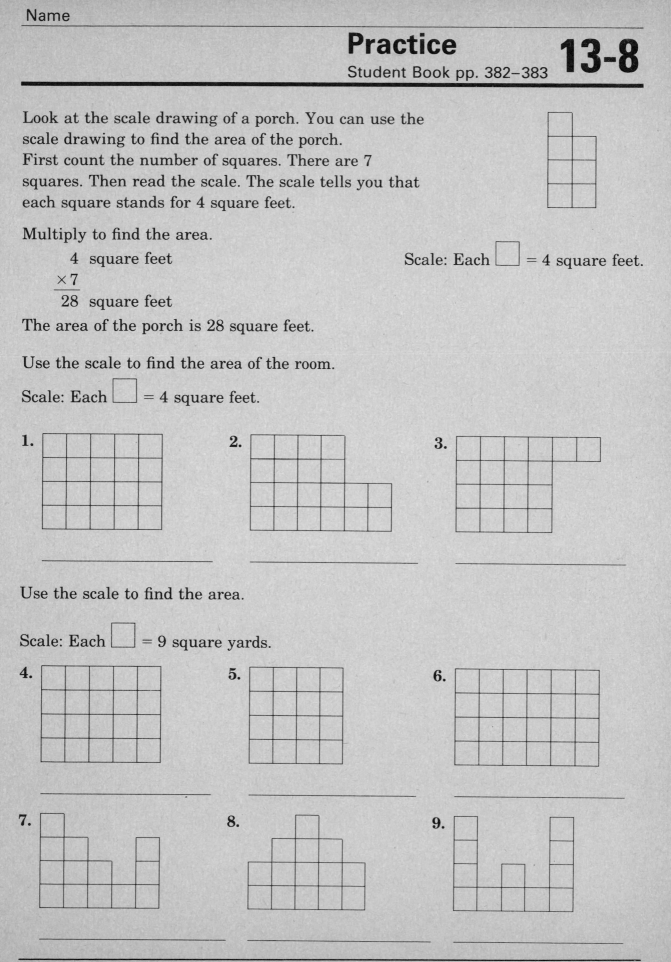

Multiply to find the area.

   4 square feet

  ×7

  28 square feet

Scale: Each ☐ = 4 square feet.

The area of the porch is 28 square feet.

Use the scale to find the area of the room.

Scale: Each ☐ = 4 square feet.

1. _____

2. _____

3. _____

Use the scale to find the area.

Scale: Each ☐ = 9 square yards.

4. _____

5. _____

6. _____

7. _____

8. _____

9. _____

Practice

Study these figures. Then complete the chart.

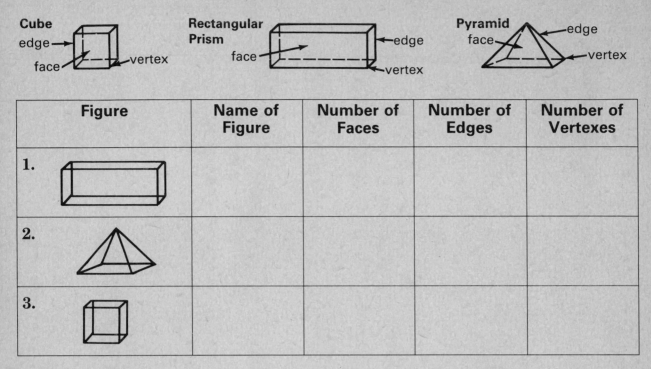

Figure	Name of Figure	Number of Faces	Number of Edges	Number of Vertexes
1.				
2.				
3.				

How would the first figure look from the bottom? Write the letter.

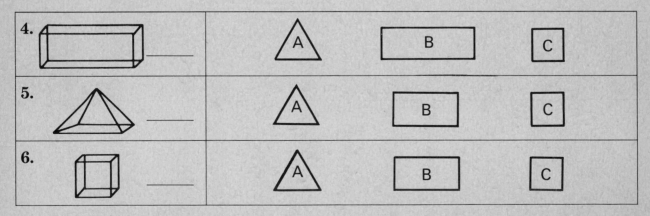

4. ____	A / B	C
5. ____	A / B	C
6. ____	A / B	C

These shapes can be folded to form a cube, a rectangular prism, or a pyramid. Name the shape that can be formed.

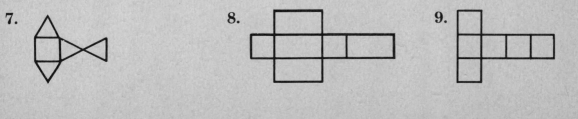

7. _____

8. _____

9. _____

Practice

Student Book pp. 386–387

Study these figures. Then complete the chart.

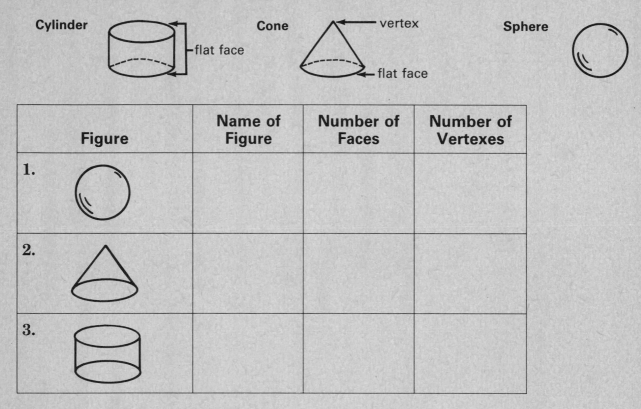

Cylinder —flat face   Cone — vertex / — flat face   Sphere

Figure	Name of Figure	Number of Faces	Number of Vertexes
1.			
2.			
3.			

How would the first figure look from the side? Write the letter.

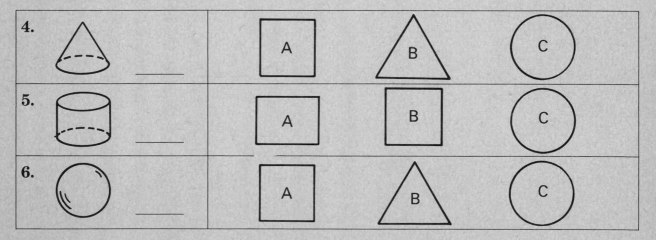

4.	A	B	C
5.	A	B	C
6.	A	B	C

Picture the answer in your mind then draw it.

7. If you cut a cylinder in half along the line shown, what would the new faces be? _____

8. If you cut a cone along the line shown, what would the new faces be? _____

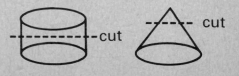

---cut   --- cut

Practice

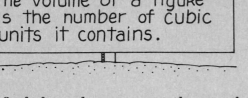

The volume of a figure is the number of cubic units it contains.

A cubic centimeter is often used as a cubic unit.

1 cm   1 cm   1 cm

one cubic centimeter

To find the volume, count the number of cubic centimeters in this figure.

The volume of this figure is 16 cubic centimeters.

What is the volume? Complete.

1.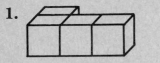

_____ cubic centimeters

2.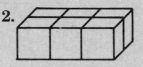

_____ cubic centimeters

3.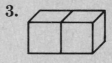

_____ cubic centimeters

4.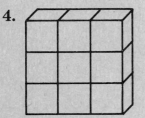

_____ cubic centimeters

5.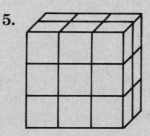

_____ cubic centimeters

6.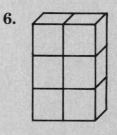

_____ cubic centimeters

These buildings were designed using cubic units.

Solve.

7. Which building has the greater volume? _____

8. Which building covers the most ground? _____

9. Which building has the greater distance around it? _____

A

B

To find the volume of this box, you can multiply.

There are 8 cubic centimeters in each layer.

$$2 \times 4 = 8$$

The box has 3 layers with 8 cubic centimeters in each layer.

$$3 \times 8 = 24$$

The volume of the box is 24 cubic centimeters.

What is the volume? Be sure to write the correct units.

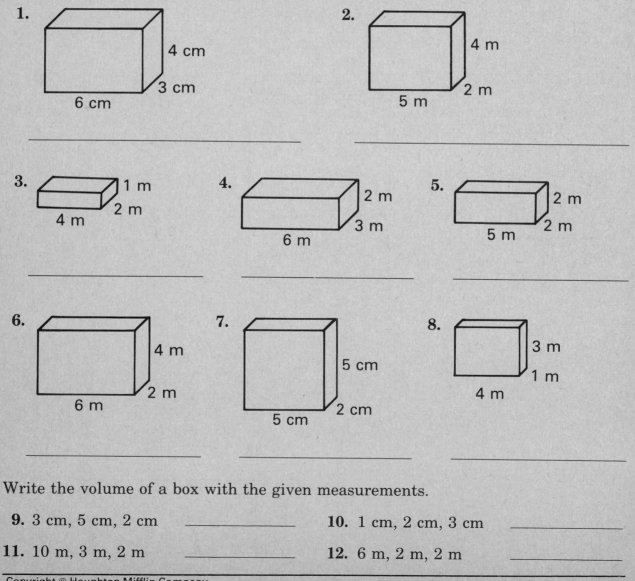

1. 4 cm 3 cm 6 cm

_____

2. 4 m 2 m 5 m

_____

3. 1 m 2 m 4 m

_____

4. 2 m 3 m 6 m

_____

5. 2 m 2 m 5 m

_____

6. 4 m 2 m 6 m

_____

7. 5 cm 2 cm 5 cm

_____

8. 3 m 1 m 4 m

_____

Write the volume of a box with the given measurements.

9. 3 cm, 5 cm, 2 cm _____

10. 1 cm, 2 cm, 3 cm _____

11. 10 m, 3 m, 2 m _____

12. 6 m, 2 m, 2 m _____

Here is a sketch of Meg's flower garden.

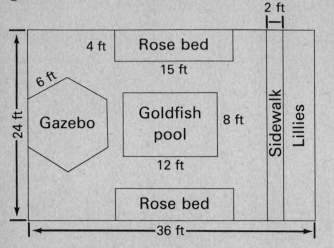

Tell whether the problem asks you to find perimeter, area, or volume. Write *p*, *a*, or *v*. Then solve.

1. Meg wants to use a canvas top to cover the goldfish pool during the winter. How much space must the top cover? ____ _____

2. Meg wants to put a two-foot high railing around the floor of the gazebo. How many feet of railing does she need? ____ _____

3. How much space does Meg's flower garden cover in all? ____ _____

4. How much space does the sidewalk take up in the flower garden? ____ _____

5. The goldfish pool is 1 ft deep. How much water does it hold? ____ _____

6. Meg is planting a row of flowers around the edge of the goldfish pool. How long will the row be? ____ _____